FOUNDATIONS OF MODERN CHEMISTRY

A Comprehensive Guide for Degree Students

SREEKUMAR V T

PREFACE

Welcome to "Foundations of Modern Chemistry: A Comprehensive Guide for Degree Students." This book is crafted with the explicit purpose of providing an in-depth and accessible exploration of the fundamental principles that underpin modern chemistry, tailored specifically for students pursuing degrees in the field. As you embark on your academic journey, this guide aims to be your reliable companion, offering a structured and comprehensive approach to the diverse landscape of contemporary chemistry.

In the ever-evolving realm of scientific discovery, a solid understanding of foundational principles is crucial. This text is designed to instil a deep appreciation for the core concepts that form the bedrock of modern chemistry. Whether you are just beginning your degree or seeking to reinforce your knowledge, each chapter is carefully crafted to build upon the last, facilitating a seamless progression through the intricacies of the subject.

Key Features:

1. **Comprehensive Coverage:** The book encompasses a wide range of topics, from atomic structure and chemical bonding to advanced areas such as quantum mechanics and environmental chemistry. This breadth ensures a holistic understanding of the discipline.
2. **Clarity of Presentation:** Complex theories and principles are presented with clarity, employing a step-by-step approach to help students navigate through intricate concepts. Real-world examples and applications are incorporated to enhance comprehension and relevance.

3. **Integration of Modern Research:** The text incorporates recent advancements in the field, highlighting the dynamic and ever-expanding nature of modern chemistry. This integration serves to inspire students and emphasizes the practical implications of theoretical concepts.
4. **Practical Applications:** A strong emphasis is placed on the practical applications of chemical principles. Chapters include examples and exercises that encourage critical thinking and the application of theoretical knowledge to real-world scenarios.

As authors, our goal is to foster a passion for learning and curiosity about the world of chemistry. We recognize the challenges that degree students may face, and this guide is designed to serve as a supportive resource throughout your academic journey.

We invite you to delve into the pages of "Foundations of Modern Chemistry" and embark on a rewarding exploration of the essential principles that shape the discipline. May this guide illuminate your path, enrich your understanding, and inspire your pursuit of knowledge in the fascinating realm of modern chemistry.

Happy reading and best wishes on your academic endeavours!

SREEKUMAR V T

COPYRIGHT WARNING

CONTENTS

1. INTRODUCTION TO CHEMICAL PRINCIPLES

C hemistry, often referred to as the central science, forms the bridge between the microscopic and macroscopic realms of our world. At its core lies a rich tapestry of principles that govern the behaviour of matter. In the journey through the foundations of modern chemistry, we begin with the bedrock—the Introduction to Chemical Principles. This fundamental understanding serves as the cornerstone upon which the edifice of chemical knowledge is built, laying the groundwork for degree students to navigate the complexities of the molecular world.

The Essence of Chemical Principles

At its essence, chemical principles encompass the fundamental concepts that govern the composition, structure, properties, and reactions of matter. It is the language through which chemists communicate with the universe, deciphering the secrets of atoms and molecules. Our exploration begins with an inquiry into the atom—the indivisible building block of matter.

The Atom: A Microscopic Marvel

The journey commences with the atom, an entity so small that its dimensions elude direct observation. Yet, within this minuscule domain, a universe unfolds. We unravel the nucleus, housing protons and neutrons, and the enigmatic electron cloud that defines the atom's size and reactivity. The periodic table, a map of the atomic landscape, becomes our guide, revealing patterns that dictate the behaviour of elements.

Chemical Bonding: Forces That Bind

2.ATOMIC STRUCTURE AND THE PERIODIC TABLE

n the grand tapestry of chemistry, the atom stands as the fundamental unit, the building block that constructs the intricate structures of the material world. As we embark on the journey through the oundations of Modern Chemistry: A Comprehensive Guide for Degree dents," our exploration begins with a profound inquiry into atomic cture and its manifestation in the Periodic Table. This chapter serves as teway, unveiling the microscopic architecture that underlies the rsity of matter and the systematic organization that governs its aviour.

The Atom: An Indivisible Essence

The concept of the atom, once considered an indivisible entity, has evolved through centuries of scientific inquiry. We trace the historical milestones from Democritus' early notion of "Atomos" to Dalton's atomic theory, which laid the groundwork for our modern understanding. The atom, though invisible to the naked eye, is a dynamic entity, a miniature universe governed by the laws of quantum mechanics.

Nucleus: The Central Command

At the heart of the atom lies the nucleus, a compact region housing rotons and neutrons. We delve into the role of these subatomic articles, understanding how the positive charge of protons is alanced by the neutral presence of neutrons. The nucleus emerges as e command centre, dictating the identity of the atom and fluencing its properties.

Having acquainted ourselves with individual atoms, we turn to the forces that bind them together. Chemical bonding emerges as a pivotal concept, exploring the various interactions that create compounds. From ionic bonds that result from the transfer of electrons to covalent bonds formed through electron sharing, we delve into the intricacies of molecular architecture.

Stoichiometry: Balancing the Equation

Equipped with a grasp of atomic interactions, we venture into stoichiometry—a quantitative exploration of chemical reactions. Balancing equations becomes an art, unveiling the conservation of mass and the quantitative relationships that govern reactions. This fundamental skill serves as the foundation for understanding the vast landscape of chemical transformations.

Thermodynamics: Heat, Work, and Energy Changes

As our journey unfolds, we encounter the realm of thermodynamics —an exploration of energy and its transformations. From the laws of thermodynamics to the concept of entropy, we delve into the driving forces behind chemical processes. Thermodynamics not only unveils the spontaneity of reactions but also serves as a guide in understanding the dynamic interplay of energy in the molecular world.

Chemical Kinetics: Rates of Reaction

In the dynamic theatre of chemical reactions, kinetics takes centre stage. Chemical kinetics explores the rates at which reactions occur, unveiling the factors that influence reaction speed. From collision theory to reaction mechanisms, we embark on a journey through the temporal dimension of chemical processes.

Equilibrium in Chemical Systems

Equilibrium, a delicate balance between opposing forces, governs chemical systems. Le Chatelet's principle becomes our guiding light as we navigate the conditions that influence the position of equilibrium. Understanding equilibrium is not only crucial for predicting reaction outcomes but also for manipulating systems to achieve desired results.

Acids and Bases: The Bronsted-Lowry and Lewis Definitions

The acidity and basicity of substances shape a myriad of chemical processes. We explore the definitions of acids and bases through the lens of Bronsted-Lowry and Lewis, uncovering the intricate dance of protons in aqueous solutions. Acid-base equilibria emerge as a fundamental aspect, influencing everything from biological systems to industrial processes.

Electrochemistry: Redox Reactions and Electrolysis

The dance of electrons takes centre stage in electrochemistry. Redox reactions, characterized by electron transfer, form the backbone of this discipline. From voltaic cells to electrolysis, we explore the practical applications of electrochemical principles, delving into the world of batteries, corrosion, and electroplating.

Introduction to Quantum Mechanics

At the heart of the molecular realm lies quantum mechanics—a theoretical framework that challenges our classical intuition. From wave-particle duality to the Heisenberg uncertainty principle, we confront the peculiarities that define the behaviour of particles at the atomic and subatomic levels. Quantum mechanics becomes the key to understanding electronic structure and the foundations of chemical bonding.

Molecular Orbital Theory and Electronic Structure

Building upon our understanding of quantum mechanics, we delve into molecular orbital theory. This advanced concept allows us to visualize the distribution of electrons in molecules, providing insights into their stability and reactivity. The electronic structure becomes a blueprint, guiding us in predicting the properties and behaviour of complex molecular systems.

Organic Chemistry Fundamentals

In the organic realm, carbon takes the spotlight, forming th of countless compounds essential to life. Organic chemistr introduces us to the diverse array of hydrocarbons, functic and reaction mechanisms that characterize this branch of discipline. From alkanes to aromatics, we unravel the lan organic molecules.

Inorganic Chemistry: Transition Metals and Coordinatic

Transition metals add a layer of complexity to our expl introducing new bonding paradigms and electronic cor Coordination complexes, with their vibrant colors and structures, become the focus of our inquiry. Inorganic showcases the diversity of elements beyond the main expanding our understanding of the periodic table.

Environmental Chemistry and Sustainable Practices

As stewards of the planet, our journey concludes w of the environmental impact of chemical processes chemistry explores the fate and transport of pollut of the atmosphere, and sustainable practices that r ecological footprint of human activities.

Conclusion: A Foundation for Future Exploratio

The journey through the Introduction to Chemic an initiation and an invitation. It lays the found exploration of the molecular world, setting the studies and real-world applications. Armed wi guide, degree students are empowered to navi landscape of modern chemistry with confider to unravel the mysteries of the microscopic r

In the forthcoming chapters of "Foundation Comprehensive Guide for Degree Students continues, building upon these principles t multifaceted facets of this dynamic and ev

Electron Cloud: The Enigmatic Dance

Surrounding the nucleus is the electron cloud, a vast and probabilistic region where electrons orbit in distinct energy levels. We grapple with the dual nature of electrons—simultaneously behaving as particles and waves—introduced by the wave-particle duality of quantum mechanics. This dynamic dance of electrons determines the atom's size and its interactions with other atoms.

Quantum Numbers and Electron Configurations

The quantum mechanical model provides a robust framework for understanding the distribution of electrons in an atom. We explore the significance of quantum numbers in defining an electron's location and energy state. The concept of electron configurations unveils the systematic arrangement of electrons within energy levels and sublevels, offering a blueprint for the atom's behaviour.

The Periodic Table: A Symphony of Elements

As we transition from the microcosm of the atom to the macrocosm of chemical elements, the Periodic Table takes centre stage. Its elegant organization reflects the underlying principles of atomic structure and facilitates a systematic understanding of element properties and behaviours.

Mendeleev's Vision: A Prelude to Organization

We delve into the historical development of the Periodic Table, from the early attempts of categorization to Mendeleev's ground-breaking insight. The Russian chemist's recognition of periodic trends and the arrangement of elements based on atomic mass laid the foundation for the modern Periodic Table.

Modern Periodic Law: Patterns and Trends

The Modern Periodic Law becomes our guiding principle as we navigate the table's rows and columns. Periodicity, the repetition of patterns, emerges as a key theme. We unravel the significance of atomic number in organizing elements, exploring trends in atomic size, ionization energy, electronegativity, and chemical reactivity across periods and down groups.

The Elements: A Symphony of Diversity

Each element in the Periodic Table possesses a unique identity defined by its atomic number and distinct properties. We embark on a survey of the major elemental groups, from alkali metals to noble gases, unravelling their characteristics and contributions to the chemical landscape. The transition metals, nestled in the centre, exhibit a rich diversity of properties and form the bridge between main group elements.

Metalloids and Non-metals: Bridging Divides

The Periodic Table not only organizes elements based on their properties but also highlights the division between metals, metalloids, and non-metals. We explore the unique characteristics of metalloids, elements that straddle the divide, and the contrasting features of non-metals, crucial players in the formation of diverse compounds.

Beyond the Table: Unravelling the Unknown Elements

Our exploration extends beyond the confines of the known elements as we contemplate the synthesis and discovery of new elements. The quest for super heavy elements challenges our understanding of atomic structure and pushes the boundaries of the Periodic Table.

Conclusion: A Blueprint for Chemical Understanding

In the vast expanse of modern chemistry, the chapters on atomic structure and the Periodic Table serve as a foundation—a blueprint that demystifies the microscopic world and unveils the systematic organization governing the behaviour of matter. Armed with this knowledge, degree students are equipped to navigate the complexities of chemical reactions, molecular interactions, and the diverse landscape of the elements.

As our journey through the "Foundations of Modern Chemistry" unfolds, the insights gained from atomic structure and the Periodic Table will continue to resonate. From chemical bonding to advanced quantum mechanics, this foundational knowledge forms the scaffolding upon which the edifice of chemical understanding is erected. With each chapter, the intricate dance of electrons, the symphony of elements, and the elegance of periodicity will illuminate the path forward, guiding students toward a comprehensive mastery of the molecular world.

3. CHEMICAL BONDING

Ionic and Covalent Bonds

I n the microscopic realm of chemistry, where atoms and molecules reign supreme, the concept of chemical bonding emerges as a fundamental pillar upon which the understanding of matter is built. As we navigate the "Foundations of Modern Chemistry: A Comprehensive Guide for Degree Students," our exploration begins with a deep dive into the intricate world of chemical bonding, unravelling the forces that bind atoms together and shape the diverse structures of the material world.

Introduction to Chemical Bonding: The Glue of the Molecular World

Chemical bonding is the invisible force that transforms individual atoms into the myriad compounds that populate our world. It is the glue that binds atoms together, dictating the properties and behaviours of substances. The two primary types of chemical bonds—ionic and covalent—serve as the cornerstone of our inquiry, offering insights into the dynamic dance of electrons and the formation of stable molecular entities.

The Role of Electrons: Architects of Bonding

At the heart of chemical bonding lies the electron, a subatomic particle that dictates the behaviour of atoms. We delve into the significance of the outermost electrons, known as valence electrons, which play a pivotal role in the formation of chemical bonds. The desire of atoms to achieve stable electron configurations drives the intricate choreography of bonding.

Ionic Bonds: Electrons in Transit

Our journey into chemical bonding begins with ionic bonds—a phenomenon observed in the marriage between elements with vast differences in electronegativity. We explore the transfer of electrons from one atom to another, giving rise to ions with opposing charges. The electrostatic attraction between these charged entities creates the robust ionic bonds that characterize compounds like sodium chloride.

Ion Formation: The Birth of Charged Entities

Ionic bonds are born through the process of ion formation. We scrutinize the steps involved, from electron loss by metals to electron gain by non-metals. The resulting cations and anions, with their complementary charges, set the stage for the assembly of ionic compounds, showcasing the stability achieved through electrostatic interactions.

Properties of Ionic Compounds: Order in the Crystal Lattice

The properties of ionic compounds emerge from the ordered arrangement of ions in a crystal lattice. We explore the structural intricacies that contribute to the high melting points, electrical conductivity, and solubility characteristics exhibited by these compounds. The dissolution and dissociation of ions in water further illustrate the dynamic nature of ionic bonds.

Applications of Ionic Compounds: Beyond the Classroom

The relevance of ionic compounds extends beyond the laboratory, finding applications in everyday life. From the electrolyte solutions essential for batteries to the vibrant colors of transition metal complexes, the impact of ionic bonding resonates in diverse fields.

Covalent Bonds: Electron Sharing in Harmony

Transitioning from the transfer of electrons, we enter the realm of covalent bonds—a union forged through the sharing of electrons between atoms. This intimate connection creates molecular entities with shared electron clouds, imparting stability to a vast array of compounds.

Lewis Structures: Mapping Electron Sharing

To visualize the sharing of electrons, we employ Lewis structures—a tool that delineates the arrangement of valence electrons in a molecule. We unravel the rules governing Lewis structures, from the octet rule to the role of formal charge, providing a blueprint for understanding the electron distribution in covalent compounds.

Polarity in Covalent Bonds: Balancing Acts

Covalent bonds, while founded on electron sharing, can exhibit polarity. We explore the concept of electronegativity—a measure of an atom's ability to attract shared electrons—and how it influences the distribution of charge within a molecule. Polar and nonpolar covalent bonds set the stage for understanding the overall polarity of molecules.

Multiple Bonds: Strengthening the Connection

In the symphony of covalent bonding, multiple bonds—double and triple bonds—add depth to molecular structures. We unravel the forces at play in these intensified connections, exploring resonance structures and their impact on molecular stability.

Molecular Shapes: The Geometry of Covalent Bonds

The spatial arrangement of atoms in a molecule, governed by valence shell electron pair repulsion (VSEPR) theory, determines its shape and properties. We embark on a journey through molecular geometries, from linear to tetrahedral, elucidating the influence of electron pairs on the three-dimensional structure of molecules.

Comparing Ionic and Covalent Bonds: Bridging the Divide

As we traverse the landscapes of ionic and covalent bonding, we draw comparisons between these two fundamental types of chemical connections. The electronegativity difference, nature of bonding, and resulting properties provide a lens through which we understand the diverse behaviour of compounds in both categories.

Conclusion: Bonding as a Gateway to Complexity

In the exploration of chemical bonding—both ionic and covalent—we uncover the intricacies that govern the molecular world. From the simplicity of electron transfer to the nuanced dance of electron sharing, these bonds form the foundation upon which the edifice of chemical understanding is constructed. Armed with this knowledge, degree students are equipped to decipher the language of molecules, predict the behaviour of substances, and embark on a journey through the diverse landscapes of modern chemistry.

As our expedition through the "Foundations of Modern Chemistry" continues, the insights gained from the study of chemical bonding serve as a gateway to further complexity. The subsequent chapters will build upon this foundation, exploring advanced topics in molecular interactions, chemical reactions, and the dynamic interplay of forces that shape the ever-evolving field of chemistry.

4.MOLECULAR GEOMETRY AND VSEPR THEORY

I n the intricate dance of atoms and electrons that forms the essence of modern chemistry, the exploration of molecular geometry stands as a crucial chapter. As we navigate the "Foundations of Modern Chemistry: A Comprehensive Guide for Degree Students," our focus turns to the three-dimensional structures that define the behaviour and properties of molecules. At the heart of this exploration lies the Valence Shell Electron Pair Repulsion (VSEPR) theory—a guiding principle that unveils the spatial arrangement of atoms in a molecule, shedding light on the rich tapestry of molecular geometry.

Introduction to Molecular Geometry: Beyond the Flat World of Lewis Structures

While Lewis structures provide a valuable two-dimensional blueprint of molecular connectivity, they fall short in capturing the true spatial arrangement of atoms in a molecule. Molecular geometry emerges as the next layer of understanding, introducing the three-dimensional nature of molecules—a realm where the angles and distances between atoms play a pivotal role in determining molecular properties.

The Influence of Electron Pairs: A Dynamic Force in Molecular Arrangement

Electron pairs, whether bonding or nonbonding, are dynamic entities that exert a profound influence on molecular geometry. The repulsion between these electron pairs, governed by the VSEPR theory, serves as the guiding force that dictates the spatial orientation of atoms around a central atom.

The Valence Shell Electron Pair Repulsion (VSEPR) Theory: An Elegant Blueprint

At the heart of our exploration lies the VSEPR theory—an elegant and intuitive model that allows us to predict the geometric shapes of molecules based on the repulsion between electron pairs in the valence shell of an atom. We delve into the key principles that underlie VSEPR theory, from the hierarchy of repulsions to the determination of molecular shapes based on the number of bonding and nonbonding electron pairs.

Steric Number and Electron Domains: Quantifying Molecular Complexity

Central to the application of VSEPR theory is the concept of steric number, a quantitative measure that encapsulates the total number of electron domains around a central atom. We unravel the relationship between steric number and molecular shape, exploring how variations in electron domains give rise to diverse geometries.

Basic Molecular Shapes: The Building Blocks of Complexity

Armed with the principles of VSEPR theory, we embark on a journey through the basic molecular shapes. From linear and trigonal planar to tetrahedral and octahedral, each shape is a testament to the repulsive forces that govern molecular geometry. We explore the role of lone pairs in distorting these shapes and introducing asymmetry.

Advanced Molecular Shapes: The Nuances of Complexity

The molecular world, however, is not limited to the basic shapes alone. We delve into the nuances of advanced molecular shapes, from trigonal bipyramidal to seesaw and square pyramidal, unravelling the subtleties introduced by variations in steric number and lone pair arrangement. Each shape becomes a unique fingerprint, defining the identity and properties of the molecule.

Applications of VSEPR Theory: Illuminating Molecular Realities

The utility of VSEPR theory extends far beyond the confines of theoretical understanding. We explore its applications in predicting molecular polarity, elucidating the behaviour of isomers, and rationalizing the diverse properties of compounds. From the structure of simple diatomic molecules to the complexity of large biomolecules, VSEPR theory provides a powerful tool for deciphering the spatial arrangement of atoms in diverse chemical systems.

Biological Implications: VSEPR in Biomolecular Structures

In the realm of biology, VSEPR theory finds application in understanding the three-dimensional structures of biomolecules. From the helical twists of DNA to the intricate folding patterns of proteins, the principles of VSEPR guide us in deciphering the complex architectures that underlie life itself.

Technological Insights: VSEPR in Nanotechnology and Materials Science

Beyond the biological realm, VSEPR theory plays a crucial role in the design and understanding of nanomaterials. The spatial arrangement of atoms in nanoclusters and nanoparticles, as well as the properties of advanced materials, can be elucidated through the principles of VSEPR theory, offering insights with profound technological implications.

Challenges and Extensions of VSEPR Theory: Navigating Molecular Complexity

While VSEPR theory provides a powerful framework for understanding molecular geometry, it is not without its limitations. We explore the challenges and extensions of VSEPR theory, from deviations in actual molecular geometries to the role of molecular orbitals in shaping the three-dimensional landscape of molecules.

Deviations from Ideal: Realities of Molecular Behaviour

Real-world molecules often deviate from the idealized shapes predicted by VSEPR theory. We examine the factors that contribute to these deviations, including the influence of electronegativity, the presence of multiple bonds, and the effects of molecular symmetry.

The interplay of these factors adds layers of complexity to our understanding of molecular geometry.

Molecular Orbitals: A Quantum Mechanical Perspective

To address the limitations of VSEPR theory, we delve into the realm of molecular orbitals—a quantum mechanical perspective that offers a more nuanced understanding of electron distribution in molecules. We explore the concept of hybridization and its role in shaping molecular geometry, bridging the gap between classical and quantum mechanical models.

Conclusion: From Theory to Understanding

In the exploration of molecular geometry and VSEPR theory, we embark on a journey that transcends the flat world of Lewis structures, delving into the three-dimensional universe that defines the behaviour and properties of molecules. Armed with the principles of VSEPR theory, degree students are equipped to decipher the complex language of molecular shapes and predict the properties of substances with precision.

As our expedition through the "Foundations of Modern Chemistry" continues, the insights gained from the study of molecular geometry will resonate in subsequent chapters. From the intricacies of chemical bonding to the dynamic world of reaction mechanisms, this foundational knowledge serves as a guide, illuminating the path toward a comprehensive mastery of the molecular landscape.

5.STOICHIOMETRY

Balancing Chemical Equations

In the intricate world of chemistry, where atoms and molecules engage in dynamic dances of transformation, the concept of stoichiometry stands as a cornerstone. As we delve into the "Foundations of Modern Chemistry: A Comprehensive Guide for Degree Students," our focus turns to the fundamental principles of stoichiometry—a discipline that not only balances chemical equations but also unveils the quantitative relationships that underpin reactions. In this exploration, we embark on a journey to decipher the language of chemical transformations and understand how matter is conserved and transformed in the alchemical processes of the molecular world.

Introduction to Stoichiometry: Decoding the Language of Reactions

At its essence, stoichiometry is the study of the quantitative relationships between reactants and products in a chemical reaction. It provides a roadmap for understanding the proportions in which elements and compounds combine, offering insights into the composition and behaviour of substances. Stoichiometry serves as the bridge between the symbolic realm of chemical equations and the tangible world of measurable quantities.

Balancing Chemical Equations: The Art of Conservation

The journey into stoichiometry commences with the skilful art of balancing chemical equations. We explore the significance of this process, understanding how it reflects the conservation of mass—the foundational principle that matter is neither created nor destroyed in a chemical reaction. Balancing equations becomes a dance of coefficients, ensuring that the number of atoms of each element on the reactant side equals the number on the product side.

The Mole: A Quantitative Unit of Counting

Central to stoichiometry is the concept of the mole—a unit that bridges the microscopic world of atoms and molecules with the macroscopic world of everyday measurements. We delve into Avogadro's number, the mole concept, and the role of the mole in quantifying the amounts of substances involved in chemical reactions. The mole becomes our counting unit, allowing us to traverse seamlessly between the realms of particles and mass.

Chemical Formulas and Equations: The Language of Stoichiometry

Before we can embark on the quantitative journey of stoichiometry, we must first decipher the language of chemical formulas and equations. We explore the conventions of representing substances with chemical symbols and formulas, understanding how chemical equations encapsulate the essence of reactions. The stoichiometric coefficients in balanced equations become the key to unlocking the quantitative relationships between reactants and products.

The Role of Empirical and Molecular Formulas

In the realm of stoichiometry, the determination of empirical and molecular formulas takes centre stage. We dissect the steps involved in finding the simplest whole-number ratio of atoms in a compound, as well as the formula that represents the actual number of atoms in a molecule. These formulas become the foundation for stoichiometric calculations.

Stoichiometric Calculations: Navigating the Quantitative Landscape

With a firm grasp of the language of stoichiometry, we turn our attention to the quantitative calculations that define this discipline.

We explore the stoichiometric relationships between reactants and products, unveiling the methods for determining the amounts of substances involved in a chemical reaction.

Molar Mass: Bridging Mass and Moles

To navigate the quantitative landscape, we introduce the concept of molar mass—a bridge between mass and moles. We explore how molar mass allows us to convert between the mass of a substance and the number of moles it contains, providing a versatile tool for stoichiometric calculations.

Limiting Reactants and Excess Reactants: The Balancing Act

In the realm of stoichiometry, not all reactants are created equal. We unravel the concepts of limiting reactants and excess reactants, understanding how the stoichiometry of a reaction determines which reactant is fully consumed and which remains in excess. These concepts become essential for predicting reaction yields and optimizing the use of reactants.

Percent Yield: Assessing Reaction Efficiency

As chemical reactions unfold, they rarely achieve complete conversion. We introduce the concept of percent yield—a metric that assesses the efficiency of a reaction by comparing the actual yield to the theoretical yield. Percent yield becomes a valuable tool for evaluating the practical success of chemical processes.

Applications of Stoichiometry: From the Lab to Everyday Life

The principles of stoichiometry extend far beyond the confines of the laboratory, finding applications in diverse fields. We explore how stoichiometry is utilized in environmental chemistry, pharmaceuticals, and industrial processes. From understanding air pollution to optimizing drug synthesis, stoichiometry becomes a versatile tool with real-world implications.

Environmental Implications: Stoichiometry in Air Quality

In environmental chemistry, stoichiometry plays a crucial role in understanding and mitigating air pollution. We explore how the stoichiometry of combustion reactions influences the composition of air pollutants, shedding light on the importance of stoichiometric considerations in addressing environmental challenges.

Pharmaceutical Synthesis: Precision in Drug Formulation

In the pharmaceutical industry, the principles of stoichiometry guide the synthesis and formulation of drugs. We delve into how stoichiometric calculations are employed to determine reaction conditions, optimize yields, and ensure the purity of pharmaceutical products. Stoichiometry becomes an indispensable tool for precision in drug synthesis.

Industrial Processes: Efficiency in Chemical Production

From the synthesis of chemicals to the production of consumer goods, stoichiometry plays a pivotal role in industrial processes. We explore how stoichiometric considerations influence the design of chemical reactors, the optimization of reaction conditions, and the efficient use of raw materials. Stoichiometry becomes a key player in ensuring the sustainability and economic viability of industrial production.

Challenges and Extensions of Stoichiometry: Navigating Complex Systems

While stoichiometry provides a powerful framework for understanding and predicting chemical reactions, it is not without its challenges. We explore the complexities and limitations of stoichiometry, from the impact of reaction conditions to the consideration of non-ideal behaviour. The extension of stoichiometry to more advanced topics, such as reaction mechanisms and kinetics, opens the door to a deeper understanding of the dynamic nature of chemical processes.

Non-Stoichiometric Compounds: Beyond Simple Ratios

In the world of compounds, not all adhere to simple stoichiometric ratios. We delve into non-stoichiometric compounds, exploring the nuances introduced by variable composition and the role of defects in crystalline structures. Non-stoichiometric compounds challenge our traditional understanding of stoichiometry, paving the way for a deeper exploration of materials science.

Beyond Stoichiometry: Reaction Mechanisms and Kinetics

As we navigate the complexities of chemical reactions, we touch upon the realms of reaction mechanisms and kinetics. While stoichiometry provides a static snapshot of reactants and products, these advanced topics illuminate the dynamic processes that unfold at the molecular level. Reaction mechanisms become the narrative of chemical transformations, revealing the intricate steps and intermediates involved.

Conclusion: Stoichiometry as the Language of Chemical Transformations

In the exploration of stoichiometry, we unravel the language of chemical transformations—a language that allows us to quantify and predict the outcomes of reactions. Stoichiometry serves as the link between the symbolic representations of chemical equations and the measurable quantities in the laboratory. Armed with the principles of stoichiometry, degree students are equipped to decipher the quantitative intricacies of chemical reactions and navigate the diverse landscapes of modern chemistry.

As our expedition through the "Foundations of Modern Chemistry" continues, the insights gained from the study of stoichiometry will resonate in subsequent chapters. From the intricacies of chemical equilibrium to the dynamic world of thermodynamics, stoichiometry forms the bedrock upon which the edifice of chemical understanding is erected.

6.THERMODYNAMICS

Heat, Work, and Energy Changes

I n the grand tapestry of chemistry, the study of thermodynamics stands as a pivotal chapter—a gateway into the energetic heart of chemical processes. As we navigate the "Foundations of Modern Chemistry: A Comprehensive Guide for Degree Students," our focus turns to the principles that govern heat, work, and energy changes in the dynamic world of molecules. Thermodynamics, with its laws and concepts, provides the framework through which we understand the driving forces and limitations of chemical transformations.

Introduction to Thermodynamics: Unveiling the Energetic Landscape

Thermodynamics, derived from the Greek words "therme" (heat) and "dynamis" (power), is the branch of physical science that deals with the transformations of energy between different forms. At its core, thermodynamics seeks to answer fundamental questions about the spontaneity of processes, the direction of energy flow, and the maximum efficiency of work. It is the lens through which we view the energetic landscape of chemical reactions.

The First Law of Thermodynamics: Conservation of Energy

The journey into thermodynamics begins with the First Law—a statement of the principle of energy conservation. We explore how energy can neither be created nor destroyed, only transformed from one form to another. The concept of internal energy becomes our guiding light, representing the sum of the kinetic and potential energies of a system.

Work and Heat: Pathways of Energy Transfer

Within the framework of the First Law, we delve into the two pathways through which energy can be transferred—work and heat. Work is the organized transfer of energy through mechanical processes, while heat is the disorganized transfer of energy due to temperature differences. The interplay of work and heat becomes a key aspect of understanding energy changes in chemical systems.

Enthalpy and Heat Changes in Chemical Reactions

In the realm of chemistry, where reactions abound, understanding the heat changes associated with chemical processes is paramount. We introduce the concept of enthalpy—a state function that combines internal energy and pressure-volume work. Enthalpy changes, represented as ΔH, become a measure of heat flow in chemical reactions, providing insights into the thermodynamics of bond breaking and formation.

Endothermic and Exothermic Reactions: Energetic Signatures

Chemical reactions can be classified based on their heat effects. Endothermic reactions absorb heat from the surroundings, while exothermic reactions release heat. We explore how these energetic signatures manifest in everyday reactions, from combustion processes to biochemical transformations.

Calorimetry: Measuring Heat Changes Experimentally

To quantify the heat changes in a reaction, we turn to calorimetry—a technique that measures the heat absorbed or released during a chemical or physical process. We unravel the methods of constant-pressure calorimetry, where reactions occur in open containers at constant atmospheric pressure, providing a direct measure of ΔH.

The Second Law of Thermodynamics: The Direction of Spontaneity

As our exploration continues, we encounter the Second Law of Thermodynamics—a principle that governs the direction of spontaneity in processes. We delve into the concept of entropy, a measure of the disorder or randomness of a system, and explore how the universe tends towards states of higher entropy. The relationship between entropy changes (ΔS) and the spontaneity of a process becomes a guiding principle in understanding the natural flow of energy.

Gibbs Free Energy: The Driving Force of Reactions

The concept of Gibbs free energy (G) emerges as a powerful tool in predicting the spontaneity and direction of chemical reactions. We explore how Gibbs free energy combines enthalpy and entropy, offering a thermodynamic criterion for determining whether a process can occur spontaneously at constant temperature and pressure. The Gibbs free energy change (ΔG) becomes our indicator of the driving force behind chemical transformations.

Standard Gibbs Free Energy: A Reference Point for Spontaneity

To standardize our thermodynamic assessments, we introduce the concept of standard Gibbs free energy change ($\Delta G°$). This reference point allows us to predict the spontaneity of reactions under standard conditions and provides a benchmark for comparing the energetic feasibility of different processes.

Thermodynamic Cycles and Heat Engines: Harnessing Energy Transformations

The principles of thermodynamics find practical applications in thermodynamic cycles and heat engines. We explore how cyclic processes, such as the Carnot cycle, provide a theoretical framework for understanding the efficiency of heat engines. The Carnot efficiency becomes a benchmark against which the performance of real-world engines is evaluated.

Entropy in Thermodynamic Cycles: The Carnot Cycle

The Carnot cycle, a theoretical construct, allows us to explore the relationship between entropy changes and the efficiency of heat engines. We unravel the stages of the Carnot cycle, from isothermal expansion to adiabatic expansion, and understand how this idealized process sets the upper limit for the efficiency of any heat engine.

Real-world Heat Engines: The Quest for Efficiency

In the real world, no engine can achieve the ideal efficiency of the Carnot cycle. We explore the limitations imposed by irreversible processes and introduce the concept of entropy production. The quest for higher efficiency in real-world engines becomes a balancing act between thermodynamic principles and engineering constraints.

Chemical Equilibrium: A Dynamic Balance of Thermodynamic Forces

In the realm of chemical reactions, the concept of chemical equilibrium emerges as a dynamic interplay of thermodynamic forces. We explore how the equilibrium constant (K) and the reaction quotient (Q) dictate the distribution of reactants and products at equilibrium. The relationship between Gibbs free energy and equilibrium constants provides insights into the factors that influence the position of equilibrium.

Le Chatelier's Principle: Shifting Equilibrium in Response to Changes

Le Chatelier's Principle becomes our guiding light as we examine how chemical systems respond to changes in temperature, pressure, and concentration. By understanding how these changes affect the position of equilibrium, we gain insights into the factors that influence the direction of reactions and the composition of equilibrium mixtures.

Thermochemistry: A Symphony of Thermodynamic Principles in Practice

In the practical applications of thermodynamics, we turn our attention to thermochemistry—a branch that combines the principles of thermodynamics with the quantitative aspects of chemical reactions. We explore how thermochemical data, such as standard enthalpies of formation and reaction, serve as tools for predicting and assessing the energetic outcomes of reactions.

Standard Enthalpies of Formation: Benchmarking Energetic Stability

The standard enthalpy of formation ($\Delta H^\circ f$) becomes a benchmark for understanding the stability of compounds. We unravel how this thermodynamic parameter allows us to predict the heat changes associated with the formation of one mole of a substance from its elements in their standard states.

Hess's Law: The Path-Independence of Enthalpy Changes

Hess's Law becomes a powerful tool for manipulating enthalpy changes. By recognizing that enthalpy changes are path-independent, we explore how this principle allows us to calculate unknown enthalpy changes by combining known reactions.

Challenges and Frontiers in Thermodynamics: Navigating Complexity

While thermodynamics provides a robust framework for understanding energy changes in chemical systems, it is not without its challenges and frontiers. We explore the complexities introduced by non-ideal behaviour, the role of statistical thermodynamics in understanding molecular behaviour, and the application of thermodynamic principles in fields such as biochemistry and materials science.

Non-Ideal Behaviour: Deviations from Thermodynamic Ideality

In real-world systems, deviations from ideal behaviour can pose challenges to traditional thermodynamic models. We delve into the factors that contribute to non-ideal behaviour, from intermolecular forces to the limitations of classical thermodynamics. The extension of thermodynamics to statistical thermodynamics offers a deeper understanding of molecular interactions.

Thermodynamics in Biochemistry: Energetics of Life Processes

In the realm of biochemistry, thermodynamics plays a crucial role in understanding the energetics of life processes. We explore how the principles of thermodynamics govern biochemical reactions, from the metabolism of nutrients to the synthesis of biomolecules. The thermodynamics of ATP hydrolysis becomes a key example of how energy changes drive cellular processes.

Thermodynamics in Materials Science: Energetic Foundations of Materials

In materials science, thermodynamics guides the design and characterization of materials. We explore how the principles of thermodynamics influence phase transitions, material stability, and the synthesis of advanced materials. The energetic considerations in the design of alloys and the prediction of phase diagrams become essential tools in materials engineering.

Conclusion: Thermodynamics as the Energetic Compass of Chemistry

In the exploration of thermodynamics, we traverse the energetic landscape that governs the behaviour of matter. From the conservation of energy to the spontaneity of reactions, thermodynamics serves as the energetic compass of chemistry—a guide that illuminates the pathways and limits of chemical transformations. Armed with the principles of thermodynamics, degree students are equipped to decipher the energetic language of molecules and navigate the diverse landscapes of modern chemistry.

As our expedition through the "Foundations of Modern Chemistry" continues, the insights gained from the study of thermodynamics will resonate in subsequent chapters. From the intricacies of reaction kinetics to the dynamic world of quantum chemistry, thermodynamics forms the bedrock upon which the edifice of chemical understanding is erected.

7.CHEMICAL KINETICS

Rates of Reaction

I n the intricate realm of chemistry, where atoms and molecules engage in dynamic ballets of transformation, the study of chemical kinetics takes centre stage. As we delve into the "Foundations of Modern Chemistry: A Comprehensive Guide for Degree Students," our focus turns to the principles that govern the rates of reactions—the heartbeat of molecular processes. Chemical kinetics, with its laws and theories, provides the lens through which we explore the dynamic world of molecules in motion.

Introduction to Chemical Kinetics: The Pace of Molecular Change

Chemical kinetics is the branch of chemistry that explores the rates at which chemical reactions occur and the factors that influence these rates. At its core, chemical kinetics seeks to answer fundamental questions about the speed of reactions, the pathways they follow, and the mechanisms that drive molecular transformations. It is the study of time-dependent changes in chemical systems—a journey into the temporal dimension of the molecular world.

The Rate of Reaction: Defining the Motion of Molecules

The journey into chemical kinetics begins with the concept of the rate of reaction—the measure of how quickly reactants are consumed or products are formed. We explore the factors that influence reaction rates, from the nature of reactants to the presence of catalysts, setting the stage for a comprehensive understanding of the dynamics of molecular change.

Measuring Reaction Rates: Experimental Insights

To quantify the pace of molecular transformations, we delve into the experimental methods used to measure reaction rates. From monitoring changes in concentration over time to employing techniques such as spectroscopy and chromatography, we unravel the tools that allow chemists to dissect the intricacies of reaction kinetics.

The Rate Law: A Mathematical Description of Reaction Rates

As our exploration deepens, we encounter the rate law—a mathematical expression that relates the rate of a reaction to the concentrations of reactants. We explore the order of reactions and the determination of rate constants, unravelling the quantitative framework that governs the intricacies of chemical kinetics.

Order of Reaction: Unveiling the Influence of Reactant Concentrations

The order of reaction with respect to each reactant is a key parameter in the rate law. We examine the concepts of zero, first, and second order reactions, understanding how the concentration dependence of each reactant influences the overall rate of the reaction. The determination of reaction orders becomes a crucial step in unravelling the molecular choreography.

Rate Constant: The Magnitude of Molecular Motion

The rate constant (k) emerges as a fundamental parameter in the rate law, capturing the magnitude of molecular motion. We explore how the rate constant reflects the efficiency with which reactant collisions lead to successful chemical transformations. The temperature dependence of the rate constant becomes a window into the energetic landscapes that govern reaction rates.

Reaction Mechanisms: Navigating the Molecular Choreography

In the intricate world of chemical kinetics, the concept of reaction mechanisms becomes our guide to understanding the step-by-step pathways through which reactions unfold. We explore elementary reactions, reaction intermediates, and the role of catalysts in altering reaction mechanisms. The elucidation of reaction mechanisms becomes essential for predicting and controlling the rates of complex chemical processes.

Elementary Reactions: Building Blocks of Reaction Mechanisms

At the heart of reaction mechanisms lie elementary reactions—the fundamental building blocks that describe the individual steps of a chemical transformation. We delve into the concepts of molecularity and reaction order in elementary reactions, understanding how these microscopic events dictate the overall rate of a complex reaction.

Reaction Intermediates: Temporary Rest Stops in Molecular Journeys

Within the framework of reaction mechanisms, intermediates are transient species that form and disappear during the course of a reaction. We explore the role of intermediates in providing mechanistic insights, from carbocation intermediates in organic reactions to reaction pathways involving radical species. Intermediates become the temporary rest stops in the dynamic journeys of molecules.

Catalysis: Accelerating Reactions and Expanding Possibilities

The influence of catalysts on reaction rates takes centre stage as we explore the concept of catalysis. Catalysts, by providing alternative reaction pathways with lower activation energies, enhance the efficiency of chemical transformations. We unravel the principles of homogeneous and heterogeneous catalysis, understanding how catalysts open doors to new possibilities in molecular design.

Temperature and Reaction Rates: Unveiling the Energetic Landscape

In the dynamic interplay of chemical kinetics, temperature emerges as a critical factor that influences reaction rates. We explore the Arrhenius equation, a fundamental relationship that links temperature to the rate constant, unveiling the energetic landscape that governs the motion of molecules.

Arrhenius Equation: The Temperature Dependence of Reaction Rates

The Arrhenius equation provides a quantitative description of the temperature dependence of reaction rates. We delve into the Arrhenius plot, exploring how the activation energy—an energy barrier that must be overcome for a reaction to occur—shapes the temperature sensitivity of reaction rates. The Arrhenius equation becomes a tool for predicting reaction rates at different temperatures.

Reaction Energetics: Connecting Thermodynamics and Kinetics

The connection between thermodynamics and kinetics becomes apparent as we explore the relationship between reaction energetics and reaction rates. We unravel how the concepts of activation energy and reaction enthalpy influence the speed and spontaneity of reactions. The interplay between thermodynamic stability and kinetic accessibility becomes a key theme in understanding molecular behaviour.

Factors Influencing Reaction Rates: Beyond Concentrations and Temperature

As our exploration widens, we delve into additional factors that influence reaction rates beyond concentrations and temperature. We explore the role of pressure, surface area, and the nature of reactants in shaping the kinetics of chemical processes. The multifaceted nature of these factors adds layers of complexity to our understanding of molecular motion.

Pressure Effects: The Influence of Gaseous Collisions

In gaseous reactions, pressure can influence reaction rates by altering the frequency and effectiveness of molecular collisions. We explore how the concept of reaction mechanisms expands to include pressure-dependent steps, providing insights into the dynamics of gas-phase reactions.

Surface Area and Reaction Rates: The Role of Catalysts

In heterogeneous catalysis, the surface area of catalysts plays a crucial role in determining reaction rates. We unravel how catalysts provide active sites for reactions to occur on their surfaces, influencing the rates of chemical transformations. The relationship between surface area, catalytic activity, and reaction kinetics becomes a key consideration in designing efficient catalysts.

Nature of Reactants: Chemical Identities and Kinetic Behaviour

The nature of reactants becomes a central theme in understanding kinetic behaviour. We explore how the chemical identities of reactants, including their molecular structures and functional groups, influence reaction rates. From the reactivity of organic functional groups to the kinetics of redox reactions, the diverse nature of chemical systems adds richness to our exploration of molecular dynamics.

Experimental Kinetics: Insights from the Laboratory Bench

To bridge the theoretical insights of chemical kinetics with practical applications, we turn our attention to experimental kinetics. We explore techniques such as method of initial rates, integrated rate laws, and half-life determinations, gaining hands-on insights into the methodologies used by chemists to unravel the intricacies of reaction kinetics.

Method of Initial Rates: Probing the Early Stages of Reactions

The method of initial rates becomes a powerful tool for probing the early stages of reactions. By monitoring the change in concentration of reactants or products in the initial moments of a reaction, chemists can extract valuable kinetic information. We explore how this experimental approach allows for the determination of reaction orders and rate constants.

Integrated Rate Laws: Time-Dependent Kinetic Analysis

Integrated rate laws offer a time-dependent approach to kinetic analysis, providing a framework for understanding how concentrations change over the course of a reaction. We explore the integrated rate laws for zero, first, and second order reactions, connecting theoretical concepts with experimental observations. The graphical interpretation of integrated rate laws becomes a visual guide to kinetic behaviour.

Half-Life Determinations: Predicting Reaction Progress

The concept of half-life—a measure of the time required for a reactant to decrease to half its initial concentration—provides a quantitative metric for predicting reaction progress. We unravel how half-life determinations offer insights into the kinetics of radioactive decay, first order reactions, and the decay of complex chemical systems.

Challenges and Frontiers in Chemical Kinetics: Navigating Molecular Complexity

While chemical kinetics provides a robust framework for understanding the rates of molecular transformations, it is not without its challenges and frontiers. We explore the complexities introduced by multi-step reactions, the role of quantum mechanics in describing molecular motion, and the application of kinetic principles in diverse fields.

Multi-Step Reactions: Unravelling Complex Molecular Choreography

In the realm of complex reactions, multi-step processes introduce layers of intricacy to kinetic analysis. We delve into the challenges of dissecting multi-step reactions, exploring the methods used to identify and study individual reaction steps. The role of reaction intermediates and the determination of rate-determining steps become essential in unravelling the molecular choreography.

Quantum Mechanics and Kinetics: The Molecular Dance at the Quantum Level

The application of quantum mechanics to chemical kinetics opens the door to a deeper understanding of molecular motion. We explore how quantum mechanical principles, such as transition state theory and tunnelling, offer insights into the energetics and dynamics of reactions at the atomic and subatomic levels. The quantum description of molecular vibrations and rotations becomes a frontier in the pursuit of precision in kinetic analysis.

Kinetics in Interdisciplinary Fields: From Astrochemistry to Environmental Science

Beyond the traditional boundaries of chemistry, the principles of chemical kinetics find applications in interdisciplinary fields. We explore how kinetics is employed in astrochemistry to understand the formation of celestial bodies and in environmental science to model the degradation of pollutants. The role of kinetics in the design of drug delivery systems and the study of biological reactions expands the reach of chemical kinetics into diverse scientific domains.

Conclusion: Chemical Kinetics as the Timekeeper of Molecular Transformations

In the exploration of chemical kinetics, we unravel the timekeeper of molecular transformations—a discipline that quantifies the rates at which reactions occur and deciphers the underlying dynamics of molecular motion. Armed with the principles of chemical kinetics, degree students are equipped to navigate the temporal dimension of the molecular world, predicting reaction rates, unravelling reaction mechanisms, and influencing the pace of molecular change.

As our expedition through the "Foundations of Modern Chemistry" continues, the insights gained from the study of chemical kinetics will resonate in subsequent chapters. From the intricacies of chemical equilibrium to the dynamic world of quantum chemistry, chemical kinetics forms the rhythmic heartbeat upon which the edifice of chemical understanding is erected.

8.EQUILIBRIUM IN CHEMICAL SYSTEMS

I n the captivating tapestry of chemistry, equilibrium emerges as a fundamental concept, governing the delicate balance in the molecular dance of chemical systems. As we delve into the "Foundations of Modern Chemistry: A Comprehensive Guide for Degree Students," our focus turns to the principles that underpin chemical equilibrium—a dynamic state where forward and reverse reactions occur at equal rates. Equilibrium is the sculptor of stability, shaping the composition and behaviour of chemical systems with precision.

Introduction to Chemical Equilibrium: The Dance of Dynamic Balance

Chemical equilibrium is the state reached when the rates of the forward and reverse reactions in a system are equal, resulting in no net change in the concentrations of reactants and products. It is the point of dynamic balance in the molecular dance—a state where the forward and reverse processes continue, yet the overall concentrations remain constant. In this equilibrium dance, the foundations of modern chemistry find their rhythmic heartbeat.

Dynamic Nature of Equilibrium: Constant Motion in Molecular Interactions

The equilibrium state is dynamic, with molecules in constant motion. While individual molecules continue to undergo reactions, the macroscopic properties of the system—such as concentration, pressure, and temperature—remain unchanging. This dynamic nature of equilibrium is a manifestation of the perpetual molecular dance occurring on the microscopic scale.

Equilibrium in Homogeneous and Heterogeneous Systems

Equilibrium can manifest in both homogeneous and heterogeneous systems. In homogeneous equilibrium, all reactants and products exist in the same phase, such as a gaseous reaction. Heterogeneous equilibrium involves reactants and products in different phases, like a reaction involving both gas and solid phases. Understanding the characteristics of these equilibria provides insights into the diverse landscapes of chemical systems.

The Law of Mass Action: Equilibrium as a Mathematical Expression

The Law of Mass Action becomes our guide in expressing the mathematical relationship between the concentrations of reactants and products at equilibrium. We explore the equilibrium constant (K), a dimensionless expression that quantifies the ratio of product concentrations to reactant concentrations. The equilibrium constant serves as the mathematical fingerprint of a chemical system at equilibrium.

Expression of Equilibrium Constants: Formulas and Significance

The expression of equilibrium constants varies for different reactions. We delve into the formulas for equilibrium constants in terms of concentrations and pressures, exploring their significance in predicting the favourability of reactions. Equilibrium constants become powerful tools for chemists, allowing them to assess the extent of reaction completion.

Reaction Quotient: A Snapshot of Non-Equilibrium States

Before reaching equilibrium, a reaction exists in a state of disequilibrium. The reaction quotient (Q) provides a snapshot of the concentrations at any given moment, allowing chemists to predict the direction in which a reaction will proceed. By comparing Q to the equilibrium constant, we gain insights into whether a reaction will shift toward more products or more reactants.

Factors Influencing Equilibrium: Le Chatelier's Principle

Le Chatelier's Principle becomes our guiding principle in understanding how chemical systems respond to changes in conditions. This principle states that if a system at equilibrium is disturbed by an external factor, the system will adjust to counteract the change and restore equilibrium. We explore the influence of changes in concentration, pressure, and temperature on the position of equilibrium.

Effect of Concentration Changes: Shifting the Equilibrium Position

When the concentration of a reactant or product changes, the system adjusts to restore equilibrium. We unravel how an increase in the concentration of a reactant or product can shift the equilibrium position, influencing the composition of the system. Le Chatelier's Principle provides a predictive framework for understanding the consequences of concentration changes.

Pressure Changes in Gaseous Equilibria: The Role of Volume and moles

In gaseous equilibria, changes in pressure can alter the position of equilibrium. We explore how Le Chatelier's Principle applies to reactions involving gaseous species, focusing on the influence of volume changes and the relationship between moles of gas and pressure. The dynamic response of the system to pressure changes becomes a key consideration in understanding gas-phase equilibria.

Temperature Effects on Equilibrium: The Thermodynamic Influence

Temperature is a potent factor that can influence the position of equilibrium. We unravel how changes in temperature affect the value of the equilibrium constant and explore the thermodynamic principles that govern these temperature-dependent shifts. The endothermic and exothermic nature of reactions becomes a key consideration in predicting the impact of temperature changes.

Applications of Equilibrium Principles: From Industrial Processes to Environmental Dynamics

The principles of chemical equilibrium find widespread applications in diverse fields, from industrial processes to environmental dynamics. We explore how equilibrium concepts are employed in the synthesis of chemicals, the production of ammonia through the Haber-Bosch process, and the optimization of reaction conditions in various industries. Equilibrium considerations also play a pivotal role in understanding environmental processes, such as acid-base equilibria in natural waters.

The Haber-Bosch Process: Ammonia Synthesis and Equilibrium Optimization

The synthesis of ammonia through the Haber-Bosch process serves as a prime example of how equilibrium principles impact industrial processes. We unravel the complexities of this process, exploring how chemists optimize reaction conditions to achieve maximum yield while considering the economic and practical constraints of large-scale ammonia production.

Acid-Base Equilibria in Natural Waters: Environmental Implications

In environmental chemistry, the principles of acid-base equilibria govern the dynamics of natural waters. We delve into the equilibrium reactions that influence the pH of aquatic systems, exploring the buffering capacity of water and the consequences of acid rain. Equilibrium considerations become essential in understanding and mitigating the environmental impacts of anthropogenic activities.

Biological Equilibria: The Equilibrium of Life Processes

Equilibrium principles extend into the realm of biology, influencing the behaviour of biological molecules and systems. We explore how the concepts of acid-base equilibria apply to physiological processes, such as blood buffering, and how enzymatic reactions are influenced by equilibrium considerations. The delicate balance of biological equilibria underpins the harmony of life processes.

Challenges and Frontiers in Equilibrium Chemistry: Navigating Complexity

While equilibrium principles provide a powerful framework for understanding the behaviour of chemical systems, they are not without their challenges and frontiers. We explore the complexities introduced by multi-equilibria, the interplay between kinetics and equilibrium, and the application of equilibrium concepts to advanced topics such as thermodynamics and quantum chemistry.

Multi-Equilibria Systems: Juggling Dynamic Balances

In complex systems involving multiple equilibria, chemists face the challenge of juggling dynamic balances. We delve into the intricacies of multi-equilibria systems, exploring how the interactions between different equilibria influence the overall behaviour of chemical processes. The application of mathematical tools, such as simultaneous equations, becomes essential in navigating the complexity of these systems.

Kinetics and Equilibrium: A Dynamic Duo in Molecular Transformations

The interplay between kinetics and equilibrium adds layers of complexity to the understanding of molecular transformations. We explore how the principles of chemical kinetics influence the establishment of equilibrium and shape the temporal evolution of reactions. The dynamic duo of kinetics and equilibrium becomes a powerful combination in deciphering the intricacies of reaction mechanisms.

Equilibrium in Advanced Topics: Thermodynamics and Quantum Chemistry

Equilibrium concepts extend their reach into advanced topics such as thermodynamics and quantum chemistry. We unravel how equilibrium principles underpin thermodynamic relationships, including the Gibbs free energy and the thermodynamic equilibrium constant. In the realm of quantum chemistry, the application of statistical mechanics and the partition function opens new frontiers in the description of molecular behaviour at the quantum level.

Conclusion: Equilibrium as the Architect of Molecular Stability

In the exploration of chemical equilibrium, we uncover the architect of molecular stability—a dynamic state that shapes the composition and behaviour of chemical systems. Armed with the principles of equilibrium, degree students are equipped to decipher the intricate dance of molecules, predicting how changes in conditions influence the delicate balance in chemical processes.

As our expedition through the "Foundations of Modern Chemistry" continues, the insights gained from the study of equilibrium will resonate in subsequent chapters. From the intricacies of thermodynamics to the dynamic world of quantum chemistry, equilibrium forms the foundational structure upon which the edifice of chemical understanding is erected.

9.ACIDS AND BASES

The Bronsted-Lowry and Lewis Definitions

In the expansive realm of chemistry, the concepts of acids and bases stand as fundamental pillars, shaping the understanding of chemical interactions and reactions. As we navigate the "Foundations of Modern Chemistry: A Comprehensive Guide for Degree Students," our focus turns to the dual perspectives provided by the Bronsted-Lowry and Lewis definitions of acids and bases. These definitions offer complementary insights into the behaviour of substances in aqueous and non-aqueous environments, unveiling the versatile nature of acids and bases in diverse chemical landscapes.

Introduction to Acids and Bases: Classical Views and Modern Perspectives

The exploration of acids and bases begins with a historical perspective, tracing the classical definitions that laid the groundwork for modern theories. The Arrhenius definition, proposed in the late 19th century, identified acids as substances that release protons (H^+) in aqueous solution and bases as substances that release hydroxide ions (OH^-). While ground-breaking, the Arrhenius definition proved limited in its scope, prompting the development of more comprehensive theories.

Arrhenius Definition: Aqueous Protons and Hydroxide Ions

The Arrhenius definition provided a simple and effective framework for understanding acids and bases in aqueous solutions. Acids, such as hydrochloric acid (HCl), dissociate to release protons, while bases, like sodium hydroxide (NaOH), dissociate to yield hydroxide ions. This definition, however, faced limitations when applied to non-aqueous systems and molecules lacking hydroxide ions.

The Bronsted-Lowry Definition: Proton Donors and Acceptors

The limitations of the Arrhenius definition paved the way for the Bronsted-Lowry definition, which broadened the scope of acid-base interactions. In the Bronsted-Lowry model, an acid is defined as a substance capable of donating a proton (H^+), and a base is a substance capable of accepting a proton. This definition, applicable to both aqueous and non-aqueous systems, provided a more versatile and encompassing view of acid-base behaviour.

Proton Transfer Reactions: Dynamic Equilibrium in Bronsted-Lowry Acids and Bases

The essence of the Bronsted-Lowry definition lies in proton transfer reactions. We delve into the dynamic equilibrium established when an acid donates a proton to a base, forming a conjugate acid-base pair. The equilibrium constant (K) for these reactions becomes a quantitative measure of the relative strengths of acids and bases—a key aspect in understanding the acidity or basicity of a substance.

Conjugate Acid-Base Pairs: The Dynamic Duos of Bronsted-Lowry Chemistry

In the Bronsted-Lowry framework, every acid has a conjugate base, and every base has a conjugate acid. We explore the concept of conjugate acid-base pairs, understanding how the strength of an acid is inversely related to the strength of its conjugate base. This dynamic interplay between acids and their conjugates adds richness to our understanding of proton transfer reactions.

The Lewis Definition: Electron-Pair Donors and Acceptors

As our exploration deepens, we encounter the Lewis definition of acids and bases, proposed by Gilbert N. Lewis in the early 20th century. The Lewis definition expands the conceptual landscape, transcending the limitations of proton-centric views. In the Lewis model, an acid is a substance that can accept an electron pair, and a base is a substance that can donate an electron pair.

Coordination Complexes: Lewis Acids and Bases in Action

The Lewis definition finds practical applications in the formation of coordination complexes. We unravel how metal ions, acting as Lewis acids, coordinate with electron-rich species, serving as Lewis bases. The Lewis acid-base interaction becomes the driving force behind the formation of complex structures, influencing phenomena ranging from transition metal chemistry to biological processes.

Coordinate Covalent Bonds: The Lewis Language of Electron Sharing

At the heart of the Lewis definition is the concept of coordinate covalent bonds, where both electrons in a shared pair come from one species—the Lewis base. We explore how coordinate covalent bonds manifest in various chemical reactions, from the formation of metal-ligand complexes to the interactions between Lewis acids and bases in organic chemistry. The Lewis language of electron sharing provides a unified framework for understanding a broad spectrum of chemical phenomena.

Strengths and Weaknesses of Acid-Base Definitions: A Comparative Analysis

In evaluating the Bronsted-Lowry and Lewis definitions, we conduct a comparative analysis to highlight their strengths and weaknesses. While the Bronsted-Lowry model excels in describing proton transfer reactions and is widely applicable to aqueous and non-aqueous systems, the Lewis definition provides a broader perspective by encompassing electron-pair interactions. The choice of definition depends on the specific context of the chemical system under consideration.

Applicability to Non-Aqueous Systems: Lewis Definition's Versatility

One of the strengths of the Lewis definition lies in its versatility in describing acid-base interactions beyond aqueous solutions. We explore how the Lewis model is well-suited for understanding reactions in non-aqueous solvents and in the gas phase, where proton transfer may not be the predominant mode of interaction. The Lewis definition becomes a valuable tool in describing the behaviour of molecules in diverse environments.

Limitations of Lewis Acids: Anionic and Cationic Complexes

While the Lewis definition provides a comprehensive framework, it faces challenges in classifying certain species. We delve into the limitations posed by anionic and cationic complexes, where the distinction between Lewis acids and bases becomes less clear. The complexity of species with multiple electron-donating or accepting sites adds layers of ambiguity to the application of the Lewis model.

pH and pKa: Quantitative Measures of Acidity and Basicity

In the realm of acid-base chemistry, the concepts of pH and pKa serve as quantitative measures that bridge theory with practical applications. The pH scale quantifies the acidity or basicity of a solution, with lower pH values indicating higher acidity and higher pH values indicating higher basicity. The pKa value, derived from the equilibrium constant for an acid, provides a measure of its strength— a lower pKa indicates a stronger acid.

pH Scale: Gauging Acid-Base Intensity

We explore the pH scale as a logarithmic measure of hydrogen ion concentration in a solution. The neutrality of pure water at a pH of 7, acidic solutions with pH values below 7, and basic solutions with pH values above 7 form the foundation of the pH scale. The pH scale becomes a universal tool for chemists, providing a standardized language to communicate the acidity or basicity of solutions.

pKa Values: Strength of Bronsted-Lowry Acids

Derived from the equilibrium constant for a Bronsted-Lowry acid dissociation, the pKa value quantifies the strength of an acid. We unravel the relationship between pKa and acid strength, understanding how a lower pKa corresponds to a stronger acid. The pKa values of common acids become reference points for predicting the behaviour of acids in various chemical contexts.

Applications of Acid-Base Concepts: From Biological Systems to Industrial Chemistry

The principles of acid-base chemistry find wide-ranging applications in fields as diverse as biology and industrial chemistry. We explore how acid-base equilibria govern biological processes, from enzyme catalysis to blood buffering. In industrial chemistry, acid-base interactions play a crucial role in catalysis, synthesis, and the optimization of reaction conditions.

Biological Buffer Systems: Maintaining pH Homeostasis

In biological systems, maintaining pH homeostasis is essential for the proper functioning of enzymes and cellular processes. We delve into the role of biological buffer systems, such as the bicarbonate buffer system in blood, in resisting changes in pH. The interplay between weak acids and their conjugate bases becomes a key mechanism for balancing acidity in biological fluids.

Catalysis in Industrial Chemistry: Acid-Base Catalysts

In industrial chemistry, acid-base catalysis accelerates reactions and enhances reaction selectivity. We explore how acid-base catalysts facilitate reactions in processes ranging from the production of biodiesel to the synthesis of pharmaceuticals. The principles of Bronsted-Lowry and Lewis acid-base interactions become guiding principles in the design and optimization of industrial chemical processes.

Challenges and Frontiers in Acid-Base Chemistry: Navigating Complexity

While the Bronsted-Lowry and Lewis definitions provide powerful frameworks for understanding acid-base interactions, they are not without their challenges and frontiers. We explore the complexities introduced by superacid and superbases, the interplay between different acid-base theories, and the application of acid-base concepts in advanced topics such as organometallic chemistry and quantum chemistry.

Superacid and Superbases: Beyond Traditional Definitions

The exploration of superacid and superbases challenges traditional definitions and pushes the boundaries of acid-base chemistry. We delve into the characteristics of superacid, which surpass the strength of common acids, and superbases, which exhibit extraordinary basicity. The study of these extreme species opens new avenues for understanding the limits of acid-base interactions.

Integration of Acid-Base Theories: Unifying Perspectives

As our understanding of acid-base chemistry evolves, the integration of different theories becomes a frontier in unifying perspectives. We explore how the Bronsted-Lowry and Lewis definitions can be reconciled, leading to a more comprehensive understanding of acid-base behaviour. The unified approach offers a holistic view that encompasses both proton and electron transfer reactions.

Acid-Base Concepts in Advanced Topics: Organometallic and Quantum Chemistry

The application of acid-base concepts extends into advanced topics such as organometallic chemistry and quantum chemistry. We unravel how Lewis acid-base interactions play a crucial role in the reactivity of organometallic compounds, influencing processes like catalysis and bond activation. In the realm of quantum chemistry, the electronic structure of acids and bases becomes a focal point in describing molecular behaviour at the quantum level.

Conclusion: Acid-Base Chemistry as the Language of Molecular Interactions

In the exploration of acids and bases through the lenses of the Bronsted-Lowry and Lewis definitions, we uncover the language of molecular interactions—a language that transcends classical boundaries and adapts to the versatile nature of chemical systems. Armed with the principles of acid-base chemistry, degree students are equipped to decipher the intricate dance of protons and electrons, predicting the behaviour of substances in a diverse array of chemical environments.

As our expedition through the "Foundations of Modern Chemistry" continues, the insights gained from the study of acids and bases will resonate in subsequent chapters. From the complexities of chemical kinetics to the dynamic world of quantum chemistry, acid-base chemistry forms the language upon which the edifice of chemical understanding is erected.

10.ELECTROCHEMISTRY

Redox Reactions and Electrolysis

In the intricate tapestry of chemistry, electrochemistry stands as a captivating realm where the dance of electrons orchestrates the transformation of matter. As we navigate the "Foundations of Modern Chemistry: A Comprehensive Guide for Degree Students," our focus turns to the profound principles of electrochemistry, delving into the heart of redox reactions and the transformative power of electrolysis. Electrochemistry, with its application in batteries, corrosion prevention, and the synthesis of chemicals, unveils a dynamic world where electrons play a central role in shaping the future of chemical technologies.

Introduction to Electrochemistry: The Dance of Electrons

Electrochemistry is the branch of chemistry that explores the interconversion of chemical and electrical energy. At its core lies the elegant choreography of electrons, dancing between molecules and facilitating reactions that underpin a multitude of applications. Two key phenomena within electrochemistry, redox reactions and electrolysis, form the cornerstone of this exploration.

Redox Reactions: Electron Transfers in Molecular Transformations

Redox reactions, short for reduction-oxidation reactions, represent the dynamic interplay between reduction (gain of electrons) and oxidation (loss of electrons) processes. We delve into the fundamental principles of redox reactions, understanding how electrons serve as the currency of chemical change. The oxidation state, a key concept in redox reactions, becomes a guide to deciphering the electron flow in molecular transformations.

Half-Reactions: Breaking Down Redox Processes

To unravel the complexity of redox reactions, we introduce the concept of half-reactions—a partitioning of the overall reaction into separate oxidation and reduction components. We explore how half-reactions provide a clearer picture of electron transfers, allowing chemists to identify the species being oxidized and reduced. The balancing of half-reactions becomes a crucial step in achieving overall charge neutrality.

The Electrochemical Cell: Harnessing Redox Energy

The electrochemical cell emerges as the apparatus that transforms redox reactions into useful electrical energy. We explore the components of an electrochemical cell, including the anode (site of oxidation) and cathode (site of reduction), connected by an external circuit. The salt bridge, a crucial element in maintaining charge balance, facilitates the flow of ions between the two half-cells, allowing the redox reactions to proceed.

Types of Electrochemical Cells: Galvanic and Electrolytic Cells

Electrochemical cells come in two primary types: galvanic cells (also known as voltaic cells) and electrolytic cells. Galvanic cells convert chemical energy into electrical energy, providing a spontaneous source of power. In contrast, electrolytic cells use electrical energy to drive non-spontaneous redox reactions, enabling processes such as metal plating and the electrolysis of water.

Cell Potential: Measuring the Driving Force of Redox Reactions

The cell potential (Ecell) becomes a quantitative measure of the driving force behind redox reactions in electrochemical cells. We explore how the standard cell potential (E°cell) provides a reference point for predicting the spontaneity of redox processes. The Nernst equation further refines our understanding, accounting for nonstandard conditions and the influence of concentration on cell potential.

Applications of Galvanic Cells: Batteries as Portable Powerhouses

The principles of electrochemistry find widespread applications in everyday life, with batteries standing as quintessential examples of galvanic cells in action. We delve into the workings of batteries, from the common alkaline battery to the rechargeable lithium-ion battery. The electrochemical processes driving the generation and storage of electrical energy become central to the design and optimization of battery technologies.

Alkaline Batteries: Portable Power for Everyday Devices

Alkaline batteries, ubiquitous in everyday devices, provide a reliable source of power through the redox reaction between zinc and manganese dioxide. We unravel the chemistry behind alkaline batteries, exploring how the flow of electrons from zinc to manganese dioxide drives the electrochemical cell, producing a flow of electrical energy that powers flashlights, remote controls, and other household devices.

Lithium-Ion Batteries: Energy Storage for the Digital Age

In the digital age, lithium-ion batteries have emerged as the powerhouses driving portable electronic devices. We explore the electrochemical processes within lithium-ion batteries, where lithium ions shuttle between the anode and cathode, facilitating the flow of electrons and storing electrical energy. The significance of lithium-ion batteries in powering smartphones, laptops, and electric vehicles becomes evident in their widespread adoption.

Electrolysis: Harnessing Electrical Energy for Chemical Transformations

While galvanic cells provide a means of extracting electrical energy from redox reactions, electrolysis reverses the process, utilizing electrical energy to drive non-spontaneous redox reactions. We delve into the principles of electrolysis, exploring how it serves as a transformative tool in diverse applications, from metal refining to the synthesis of chemicals.

Electrolytic Cells: Driven by External Power Sources

Electrolytic cells operate under the influence of external power sources, such as batteries or direct current (DC) power supplies. We explore the setup of electrolytic cells, where electrical energy is input to initiate non-spontaneous redox reactions. The anode and cathode in electrolysis play roles opposite to those in galvanic cells, with the anode undergoing oxidation and the cathode undergoing reduction.

Metal Electroplating: Enhancing Aesthetics and Durability

One of the practical applications of electrolysis is metal electroplating, a process used to coat objects with a thin layer of metal for aesthetic or functional purposes. We unravel how metal ions from a solution are reduced and deposited onto a substrate, forming a uniform and adherent metal coating. Electroplating enhances the aesthetics and durability of objects, from jewellery to industrial components.

Challenges and Frontiers in Electrochemistry: Navigating Complexity

As electrochemistry advances, it faces challenges and explores frontiers that push the boundaries of our understanding. We delve into the complexities introduced by non-aqueous electrochemistry, the quest for sustainable energy storage, and the development of advanced materials for electrochemical applications.

Non-Aqueous Electrochemistry: Beyond Aqueous Solutions

The traditional understanding of electrochemistry often revolves around aqueous solutions, but non-aqueous electrochemistry opens new avenues. We explore how solvents other than water, such as organic solvents or ionic liquids, offer unique opportunities and challenges in electrochemical processes. The study of non-aqueous electrochemistry expands the applicability of electrochemical technologies to diverse environments.

Sustainable Energy Storage: Beyond Lithium-Ion Batteries

While lithium-ion batteries have revolutionized portable electronic devices, the search for sustainable and high-performance energy storage solutions continues. We delve into emerging technologies, such as solid-state batteries and redox flow batteries, that hold promise for addressing the limitations of current battery technologies. Sustainable energy storage becomes a focal point in the pursuit of cleaner and more efficient power sources.

Advanced Materials for Electrochemical Applications: Tailoring Properties for Performance

The development of advanced materials plays a pivotal role in enhancing the performance of electrochemical devices. We explore how materials science contributes to the design of electrodes, electrolytes, and catalysts with tailored properties. From the quest for more efficient catalysts in fuel cells to the exploration of novel materials for supercapacitors, the study of advanced materials drives innovation in electrochemistry.

Conclusion: Electrochemistry as the Symphony of Electron Movement

In the exploration of electrochemistry, we uncover a symphony where the movement of electrons orchestrates the transformation of matter into electrical energy and vice versa. Armed with the principles of redox reactions and electrolysis, degree students are equipped to decipher the language of electron dance, predicting the behaviour of substances in diverse electrochemical processes.

As our expedition through the "Foundations of Modern Chemistry" continues, the insights gained from the study of electrochemistry will resonate in subsequent chapters. From the intricacies of chemical thermodynamics to the dynamic world of quantum chemistry, electrochemistry forms the pulsating current upon which the edifice of chemical understanding is erected.

11.INTRODUCTION TO QUANTUM MECHANICS

In the vast landscape of chemistry, the principles of quantum mechanics stand as the bedrock that underpins our understanding of the behaviour of matter at the atomic and subatomic levels. As we embark on the exploration of the "Foundations of Modern Chemistry: A Comprehensive Guide for Degree Students," our focus turns to the enigmatic realm of quantum mechanics. In this article, we unravel the fundamental concepts that define quantum mechanics, delving into the wave-particle duality, quantum states, operators, and the intriguing phenomena that govern the behaviour of particles on the quantum scale.

The Birth of Quantum Mechanics: A Paradigm Shift in Science

The inception of quantum mechanics in the early 20th century marked a profound shift in our conceptualization of the physical world. Triggered by the revolutionary work of scientists like Max Planck, Albert Einstein, Niels Bohr, and Erwin Schrödinger, quantum mechanics emerged as a response to the limitations of classical physics in describing the behaviour of particles at the atomic and subatomic levels.

Planck's Quantum Hypothesis: Quanta of Energy

Max Planck's ground-breaking proposal of the quantum hypothesis in 1900 laid the foundation for quantum mechanics. Planck suggested that energy is quantized, existing in discrete packets or "quanta." This concept, initially applied to explain the behaviour of blackbody radiation, paved the way for a fundamental shift in our understanding of energy and matter.

Wave-Particle Duality: The Dual Nature of Matter and Light

The wave-particle duality principle, articulated by Louis de Broglie and confirmed by experimental evidence, challenged the classical distinction between particles and waves. Matter, such as electrons, was found to exhibit both particle-like and wave-like characteristics. The complementary nature of this duality became a cornerstone of quantum mechanics, introducing a new paradigm in the description of particles.

Quantum States and Wavefunctions: Navigating the Probability Landscape

In quantum mechanics, particles are described not by deterministic trajectories but by wavefunctions that encapsulate the probability distribution of finding a particle in a particular state. We explore the concept of quantum states and the mathematical formalism of wavefunctions, understanding how these functions represent the inherent uncertainty in the position and momentum of particles.

Schrödinger's Equation: The Quantum Mechanical Blueprint

Erwin Schrödinger's wave equation, formulated in 1926, became the central equation of quantum mechanics. We unravel the significance of Schrödinger's equation in describing the evolution of wavefunctions over time. The solutions to this equation provide the key to predicting the behavior of particles in a quantum system.

Quantum Numbers: Addressing the Quantum Address

Quantum numbers, including the principal quantum number, azimuthal quantum number, magnetic quantum number, and spin quantum number, form the quantum address that uniquely identifies an electron in an atom. We delve into the role of quantum numbers in defining the energy levels, shapes, orientations, and spin states of electrons, bringing order to the quantum realm.

Operators and Observables: The Language of Quantum Mechanics

In quantum mechanics, physical properties are associated with mathematical operators. We introduce the concept of operators and observables, exploring how operators act on wavefunctions to extract information about the state of a system. The eigenvalue-eigenfunction relationship becomes a fundamental aspect of understanding how measurements in quantum mechanics yield specific outcomes.

Hermitian Operators: Ensuring Real Eigenvalues

Hermitian operators play a crucial role in quantum mechanics, ensuring that the eigenvalues associated with observables are real. We unravel the significance of Hermitian operators in preserving the physical interpretation of quantum states and the measurement outcomes. The mathematical elegance of Hermitian operators becomes a hallmark of the precision inherent in quantum mechanics.

Uncertainty Principle: Heisenberg's Principle of Indeterminacy

Werner Heisenberg's uncertainty principle, a cornerstone of quantum mechanics, articulates the intrinsic limitations in simultaneously knowing certain pairs of complementary properties, such as position and momentum. We explore the implications of the uncertainty principle, recognizing the fundamental role it plays in defining the boundaries of precision in the quantum realm.

Quantum Mechanics in Action: The Hydrogen Atom

To illustrate the application of quantum mechanics, we delve into the quantum description of the hydrogen atom. The solution to the Schrödinger equation for the hydrogen atom yields a set of wavefunctions, known as atomic orbitals, that describe the spatial distribution of electrons. We explore the quantum numbers associated with these orbitals, providing a visual and mathematical representation of the electron cloud in a hydrogen atom.

Orbital Shapes and Energy Levels: The Quantum Blueprint of the Hydrogen Atom

The quantum numbers associated with the hydrogen atom's wavefunctions determine the shapes and energy levels of its orbitals.

We explore the distinctive shapes of s, p, and d orbitals, understanding how the quantum numbers dictate the spatial distribution and orientation of these orbitals. The quantized energy levels of the hydrogen atom become a testament to the success of quantum mechanics in describing atomic structure.

Electron Spin and Pauli Exclusion Principle: Adding Nuances to Quantum States

The inclusion of electron spin, a quantum property with two possible values (up or down), introduces additional complexity to quantum states. We explore how the Pauli exclusion principle limits the occupancy of quantum states by electrons, preventing the violation of fundamental quantum principles. The combination of spin and the exclusion principle enriches the quantum description of electrons in atoms.

Quantum Mechanics Beyond Atoms: Molecular Orbitals and Bonding

As we extend our exploration, quantum mechanics proves indispensable in describing the structure and bonding of molecules. We introduce the concept of molecular orbitals, which arise from the quantum mechanical treatment of electron interactions in molecules. The formation of covalent bonds and the prediction of molecular geometry become applications of quantum principles in the realm of chemical bonding.

Molecular Orbital Theory: The Quantum Dance of Electrons in Molecules

Molecular orbital theory provides a quantum-based model for understanding the distribution of electrons in molecules. We explore how the combination of atomic orbitals leads to the formation of molecular orbitals, representing the spatial distribution of electrons over an entire molecule. The quantum dance of electrons in molecular orbitals elucidates the stability and reactivity of molecules.

Hybridization: The Quantum Choreography of Bond Formation

The concept of hybridization, a quantum-based approach to understanding bonding in molecules, involves the mixing of atomic orbitals to form hybrid orbitals. We unravel how hybridization rationalizes the observed geometries of molecules, from the linear arrangement in sp hybridization to the trigonal bipyramidal arrangement in sp3d hybridization. The quantum choreography of hybridization guides our understanding of molecular shapes.

Challenges and Frontiers in Quantum Mechanics: Navigating the Quantum Landscape

Quantum mechanics, while immensely successful, presents challenges and frontiers that continue to captivate researchers. We explore the complexities introduced by entanglement, the quest for a unified theory of quantum gravity, and the emergence of quantum technologies that harness the unique properties of quantum systems for information processing and communication.

Entanglement: Quantum Correlations Beyond Classical Limits

Entanglement, a phenomenon predicted by quantum mechanics, describes the correlation between the quantum states of two or more particles, transcending classical limits. We delve into the mysterious nature of entanglement, exploring how changes in the state of one entangled particle instantaneously affect the state of its counterpart, even when separated by vast distances. The study of entanglement challenges classical intuitions and opens avenues for quantum information science.

Quantum Gravity: Seeking Harmony Between Quantum Mechanics and General Relativity

The quest for a unified theory that reconciles quantum mechanics with the theory of general relativity represents a frontier at the intersection of quantum physics and cosmology. We explore the challenges inherent in merging these two foundational theories, recognizing that understanding the behaviour of matter at both the quantum and cosmic scales is essential for a comprehensive understanding of the universe.

Quantum Technologies: Harnessing Quantum Properties for Innovation

The emergence of quantum technologies, including quantum computing, quantum cryptography, and quantum sensing, showcases the transformative potential of harnessing quantum properties for practical applications. We unravel the principles behind quantum technologies, recognizing how the unique features of quantum systems, such as superposition and entanglement, are leveraged to revolutionize information processing, communication, and sensing.

Conclusion: Quantum Mechanics as the Blueprint of the Microscopic Universe

In the exploration of quantum mechanics, we uncover the blueprint that defines the microscopic universe—a universe governed by the probabilistic dance of particles and the inherent uncertainty in their properties. Armed with the principles of quantum mechanics, degree students are equipped to decipher the language of the quantum realm, predicting the behaviour of matter at scales that elude classical understanding.

As our expedition through the "Foundations of Modern Chemistry" continues, the insights gained from the study of quantum mechanics will resonate in subsequent chapters. From the complexities of chemical kinetics to the dynamic world of spectroscopy, quantum mechanics forms the blueprint upon which the edifice of chemical understanding is erected.

12.MOLECULAR ORBITAL THEORY AND ELECTRONIC STRUCTURE

I n the exploration of chemical structure and bonding, Molecular Orbital (MO) Theory stands as a cornerstone, providing a quantum-based framework to understand the arrangement of electrons in molecules. As we delve into the "Foundations of Modern Chemistry: A Comprehensive Guide for Degree Students," our focus turns to the intricacies of Molecular Orbital Theory and its role in shaping the electronic structure of molecules. In this article, we will unravel the principles behind MO Theory, explore its application in understanding molecular properties, and delve into the profound insights it offers into the behaviour of electrons in complex chemical systems.

Introduction to Molecular Orbital Theory: Beyond Atomic Boundaries

Molecular Orbital Theory, a quantum mechanical model, transcends the limitations of classical valence bond theory by treating electrons as existing in orbitals that span entire molecules. This departure from localized electron pairs and bonds allows MO Theory to provide a more comprehensive description of electron distribution and behaviour.

Building Blocks of MO Theory: Atomic Orbitals and Linear Combinations

At the heart of MO Theory lies the concept of atomic orbitals (AOs), the wavefunctions that describe the distribution of electrons around individual atoms. We explore how these atomic orbitals form the basis for constructing molecular orbitals through linear combinations. The superposition of atomic orbitals in MO Theory allows for the creation of molecular orbitals that span the entire molecule.

Molecular Orbitals: The Quantum Ensemble of Electrons

Molecular Orbitals, in contrast to atomic orbitals, extend over the entire molecule. We delve into the nature of molecular orbitals, understanding how they represent the spatial distribution and energy levels of electrons in a molecule. The combination of atomic orbitals to form molecular orbitals results in a quantum ensemble that describes the electron cloud in a more nuanced and comprehensive manner.

Molecular Orbital Diagrams: Visualizing Electron Distribution

Molecular Orbital Diagrams provide a visual representation of the distribution of electrons in a molecule. We explore how these diagrams depict the energy levels and relative energies of molecular orbitals, facilitating a qualitative understanding of the electronic structure. The filling of molecular orbitals with electrons follows the Pauli exclusion principle and Hund's rule, adding layers of complexity to the electronic arrangement.

Bonding and Antibonding Orbitals: The Yin and Yang of Molecular Stability

In MO Theory, molecular orbitals come in two primary types: bonding and antibonding orbitals. We unravel how bonding orbitals result from constructive interference of atomic orbitals, stabilizing the molecule, while antibonding orbitals arise from destructive interference, introducing an element of destabilization. The delicate balance between bonding and antibonding interactions determines the overall stability of the molecule.

Homonuclear Diatomic Molecules: The MO Dance of Elements

To illustrate the application of MO Theory, we delve into the electronic structure of homonuclear diatomic molecules. Examples like hydrogen (H_2) and nitrogen (N_2) showcase how the combination of atomic orbitals in MO Theory provides insights into the stability and bonding patterns of these molecules. The interpretation of molecular orbital diagrams for homonuclear diatomic molecules becomes a fundamental exercise in applying MO Theory.

Heteronuclear Diatomic Molecules: The Interplay of Electronegativity

Extending our exploration, we investigate the electronic structure of heteronuclear diatomic molecules, where atoms of different elements combine. We unravel how the electronegativity difference between atoms influences the distribution of electrons in molecular orbitals. Examples such as the hydrogen fluoride (HF) molecule illustrate the interplay of atomic properties in shaping the electronic structure.

Electronegativity and Bond Polarity: A Quantum Perspective

The concept of electronegativity, introduced by Linus Pauling, finds a quantum interpretation in MO Theory. We explore how the electronegativity difference between atoms in a molecule influences the character of molecular orbitals, leading to the formation of polar or nonpolar bonds. The quantum perspective provided by MO Theory enhances our understanding of bond polarity beyond the classical electronegativity scale.

Polyatomic Molecules and Delocalization: The MO Symphony of Complexity

As we move beyond diatomic molecules, the complexity of molecular structure increases. Polyatomic molecules, with multiple atoms and numerous molecular orbitals, present a symphony of electronic interactions. We delve into the concept of delocalization, where electrons are spread over multiple atoms, exploring how this phenomenon contributes to the stability and unique properties of molecules.

Conjugated Systems: The Quantum Harmony of Alternating Bonds

Conjugated systems, found in molecules with alternating single and multiple bonds, exemplify the quantum harmony of delocalized electrons. We explore the electronic structure of conjugated systems, understanding how the overlapping of p orbitals results in a continuous network of delocalized molecular orbitals. This delocalization imparts distinctive properties to conjugated molecules, such as enhanced stability and unique optical properties.

Aromaticity: MO Theory Unveils the Quantum Stability of Aromatic Molecules

Aromatic molecules, characterized by a high degree of stability and unique electronic properties, find their explanation in MO Theory. We unravel how cyclic, conjugated systems with an odd number of electron pairs exhibit aromaticity. The cyclic delocalization of electrons in aromatic molecules, exemplified by benzene, showcases the quantum stability bestowed by MO Theory.

Transition Metals and Coordination Complexes: MO Theory in Transition

Transition metals, with their ability to form complex coordination compounds, introduce a new dimension to MO Theory. We explore how the d orbitals of transition metal ions participate in the formation of molecular orbitals in coordination complexes. The splitting of d orbitals, known as crystal field splitting, influences the electronic structure and properties of transition metal complexes.

Crystal Field Theory vs. Ligand Field Theory: A Quantum Duel

The understanding of electronic structure in transition metal complexes involves a quantum duel between Crystal Field Theory (CFT) and Ligand Field Theory (LFT). We compare these two theoretical frameworks, exploring how CFT simplifies the electronic structure by treating ligands as point charges, while LFT considers the specific interactions between ligands and metal d orbitals.

Electronic Configurations in Transition Metal Complexes: A Quantum Jigsaw Puzzle

The determination of electronic configurations in transition metal complexes becomes a quantum jigsaw puzzle. We unravel how the filling of d orbitals in these complexes follows the principles of MO Theory, including the Aufbau principle and Hund's rule. The complexity introduced by the interaction of ligands with metal orbitals adds a layer of richness to the electronic structure of transition metal complexes.

Challenges and Frontiers in Molecular Orbital Theory: Navigating Quantum Complexity

Molecular Orbital Theory, while powerful, faces challenges and explores frontiers that push the boundaries of our understanding. We delve into the complexities introduced by the treatment of electron correlation, the quest for accurate computational methods, and the application of MO Theory in the study of excited states and photochemical reactions.

Electron Correlation: Beyond the Independent Particle Approximation

The independent particle approximation, inherent in many applications of MO Theory, simplifies calculations but neglects the correlation between electrons. We explore the challenges introduced by electron correlation and the development of advanced computational methods, such as configuration interaction and coupled cluster methods, to capture the intricate interplay of electrons in molecular systems.

Computational Quantum Chemistry: From Ab Initio to Density Functional Theory

The application of MO Theory in computational quantum chemistry involves a spectrum of methods, from ab initio approaches that solve the Schrödinger equation directly to Density Functional Theory (DFT), a more efficient and widely used method. We unravel the principles behind these computational techniques, understanding how they balance accuracy and computational efficiency in predicting molecular properties.

Excited States and Photochemical Reactions: MO Theory in the Quantum Spotlight

MO Theory extends its reach beyond ground-state electronic configurations to the study of excited states and photochemical reactions. We explore how MO Theory provides insights into the electronic transitions that occur during absorption of light and the subsequent photochemical transformations. The application of MO Theory in the study of photochemistry adds a dynamic dimension to its role in understanding electronic structure.

Conclusion: Molecular Orbital Theory as the Quantum Architect of Chemical Structure

In the exploration of Molecular Orbital Theory, we uncover the quantum architecture that defines the electronic structure of molecules—a structure governed by the intricate dance of electrons and the delicate balance between bonding and antibonding interactions. Armed with the principles of MO Theory, degree students are equipped to decipher the language of molecular ensemble, predicting the behaviour of electrons in a diverse array of chemical systems.

As our expedition through the "Foundations of Modern Chemistry" continues, the insights gained from the study of Molecular Orbital Theory will resonate in subsequent chapters. From the dynamics of chemical reactions to the spectroscopic fingerprint of molecules, MO Theory stands as the quantum architect upon which the edifice of chemical understanding is erected.

13.ORGANIC CHEMISTRY FUNDAMENTALS

I n the expansive realm of chemistry, organic chemistry emerges as a captivating symphony, where the versatile element carbon takes centre stage, orchestrating a molecular ballet that underlies the diversity of life and countless human-made substances. As we embark on the journey through the "Foundations of Modern Chemistry: A Comprehensive Guide for Degree Students," our focus turns to the fundamental principles of organic chemistry. In this article, we will unravel the core concepts that define organic chemistry, exploring the structure, reactivity, and synthesis of carbon-containing compounds.

Introduction to Organic Chemistry: The Carbon Connection

Organic chemistry is the branch of chemistry dedicated to the study of carbon compounds, with a primary focus on those containing carbon-hydrogen (C-H) bonds. The unparalleled ability of carbon to form diverse and stable bonds, both with itself and with other elements, bestows upon organic compounds an extraordinary richness and complexity. We delve into the historical roots of organic chemistry and its evolution as a discipline that extends beyond the realm of living organisms to encompass a vast array of molecules.

Vital Role of Carbon: The Architect of Molecular Diversity

Carbon, with its unique ability to form four covalent bonds, becomes the architectural cornerstone of organic molecules. We explore the concept of hybridization, understanding how carbon atoms adopt sp3, sp2, or sp hybridization to achieve the tetrahedral, trigonal planar, or linear geometries that underlie the diversity of organic structures. The adaptability of carbon's bonding arrangements becomes a key factor in the complexity and versatility of organic compounds.

Functional Groups: The Signature Motifs of Organic Molecules

Functional groups, specific arrangements of atoms within organic molecules, confer distinct chemical properties and reactivities. We unravel the significance of functional groups as the signature motifs that define the behaviour of organic compounds. From hydroxyl groups in alcohols to carbonyl groups in ketones and aldehydes, understanding functional groups becomes essential in predicting the properties of organic molecules.

Bonding and Structure in Organic Compounds: A Molecular Tapestry

The study of organic chemistry begins with an exploration of the bonding and structure of organic compounds. We delve into the nature of sigma (σ) and pi (π) bonds, understanding how these bonds contribute to the three-dimensional structure of organic molecules. The concept of isomerism, where compounds with the same molecular formula exhibit different arrangements of atoms, adds a layer of complexity to the organic tapestry.

Structural Isomerism: Different Arrangements, Different Molecules

Structural isomerism encompasses various ways in which atoms can be arranged to form different organic compounds. We explore the distinctions between chain isomerism, where the carbon skeleton varies, and positional isomerism, where the position of functional groups changes. The recognition of structural isomers becomes a fundamental skill in decoding the molecular diversity of organic compounds.

Stereoisomerism: The Three-Dimensional Dance of Molecules

Stereoisomerism introduces a three-dimensional aspect to molecular structure, arising from the spatial arrangement of atoms in molecules. We unravel the concepts of geometric isomerism (cis-trans isomerism) and optical isomerism (enantiomers and diastereomers), understanding how the arrangement of substituents around a double bond or chiral centre imparts unique properties to stereoisomeric compounds. The study of stereochemistry becomes integral to understanding the behaviour of drugs, flavours, and other biologically active compounds.

Nomenclature: Decoding the Language of Organic Molecules

A fundamental skill in organic chemistry is the ability to name and classify organic compounds systematically. We explore the rules of IUPAC (International Union of Pure and Applied Chemistry) nomenclature, unravelling the systematic naming conventions for alkanes, alkenes, alkynes, and cyclic compounds. The language of organic molecules, as conveyed through their names, becomes a gateway to understanding their structure and reactivity.

Alkanes: The Saturated Hydrocarbons

Alkanes, or saturated hydrocarbons, serve as the foundational class of organic compounds. We delve into the nomenclature of alkanes, understanding how the systematic naming of these compounds reflects their molecular structure. The recognition of alkane isomers and the application of IUPAC rules become essential skills in navigating the nomenclature of simple and complex organic molecules.

Functional Group Nomenclature: Beyond Hydrocarbons

The introduction of functional groups expands the vocabulary of organic nomenclature. We explore how the presence of functional groups influences the naming of organic compounds, with specific rules for alcohols, ethers, ketones, aldehydes, carboxylic acids, and amines. The systematic nomenclature of functional groups facilitates clear communication and precise identification of organic structures.

Chemical Bonding Revisited: Understanding Reactivity

A profound understanding of chemical bonding is crucial for predicting and interpreting the reactivity of organic compounds. We revisit the concepts of electronegativity, bond polarity, and resonance, exploring their roles in governing the behaviour of organic molecules. The electron-pushing formalism of curly arrows becomes a tool for describing and predicting reaction mechanisms.

Electronegativity and Bond Polarity: A Spectrum of Chemical Affinities

Electronegativity differences between atoms influence the polarity of bonds in organic compounds. We explore how the polarity of bonds, ranging from nonpolar to polar covalent to ionic, impacts the reactivity of organic molecules. The electronegativity spectrum becomes a guide to understanding the distribution of electron density in different types of bonds.

Resonance: The Molecular Ensemble of Electron Delocalization

Resonance, a fundamental concept in organic chemistry, describes the delocalization of electrons within a molecule. We unravel how resonance structures represent different electron distributions in a molecule, providing a more accurate depiction of its electronic nature. The understanding of resonance enhances our ability to predict stability, reactivity, and the distribution of charge in organic molecules.

Acids and Bases in Organic Chemistry: The Proton Ballet

Acid-base reactions play a central role in organic chemistry, influencing the reactivity of functional groups and participating in crucial transformations. We explore the Bronsted-Lowry definition of acids and bases, understanding how the donation and acceptance of protons drive organic reactions. The concept of pKa becomes a quantitative measure of acidity and basicity, guiding our understanding of reaction equilibria.

Acid-Base Properties of Functional Groups: A Proton Exchange Choreography

Different functional groups exhibit distinct acid-base properties, influencing their reactivity in organic reactions. We delve into the acid-base behaviour of alcohols, amines, carboxylic acids, and other functional groups, understanding how the presence of electron-donating or electron-withdrawing groups influences their relative acidity or basicity. The proton exchange choreography becomes a key feature in the design and understanding of organic reactions.

Nucleophiles and Electrophiles: The Dance Partners of Organic Reactions

Nucleophiles and electrophiles, often referred to as the reactants in organic reactions, engage in a dance of electron sharing. We explore the definitions of nucleophiles and electrophiles, understanding how nucleophiles donate electron pairs, while electrophiles accept them. The recognition of nucleophilic and electrophilic sites in organic molecules becomes essential in predicting reaction pathways and designing synthetic routes.

Alkanes and Cycloalkanes: The Simple Hydrocarbons

Alkanes, composed solely of carbon-carbon single bonds, and cycloalkanes, their cyclic counterparts, serve as the foundational hydrocarbons in organic chemistry. We delve into the physical properties, nomenclature, and reactivity of alkanes and cycloalkanes, recognizing their role as starting materials and intermediates in organic synthesis. The exploration of their combustion reactions highlights the source of energy embedded in these simple hydrocarbons.

Conformational Analysis: The Flexibility of Alkanes

Alkanes exhibit conformational flexibility due to the rotation around carbon-carbon single bonds. We explore the concept of conformational analysis, understanding how different conformations of alkanes are related and how certain conformations are more stable than others. The study of conformational energy diagrams provides insights into the dynamics of molecular motion in alkanes.

Cycloalkanes: The Ring Structures of Organic Chemistry

Cycloalkanes, with their cyclic structures, introduce unique reactivity and isomerism. We delve into the nomenclature and isomerism of cycloalkanes, understanding how ring strain influences their stability. The exploration of reactions involving cycloalkanes, such as ring-opening and ring-closing reactions, showcases the versatility and synthetic potential of these cyclic hydrocarbons.

Alkenes and Alkynes: The Unsaturated Hydrocarbons

Alkenes and alkynes, characterized by carbon-carbon double and triple bonds, respectively, introduce unsaturation and increased reactivity to organic compounds. We explore the structure, nomenclature, and reactions of alkenes and alkynes, recognizing their pivotal role in organic synthesis. The study of addition reactions, including Markovnikov and anti-Markovnikov additions, sheds light on the radiochemistry of reactions involving unsaturated hydrocarbons.

Alkene Isomerism: Geometric Isomerism and the Cis-Trans Dilemma

Alkenes exhibit geometric isomerism due to the restricted rotation around the carbon-carbon double bond. We unravel the concept of cis-trans isomerism, understanding how different substituent arrangements influence the properties and reactivity of alkenes. The recognition of geometric isomers becomes crucial in predicting the outcomes of reactions involving alkenes.

Alkyne Reactivity: Triple Bonds and Functional Group Transformations

Alkynes, with their carbon-carbon triple bonds, display unique reactivity that distinguishes them from alkenes. We explore the nomenclature and reactions of alkynes, recognizing their role as versatile intermediates in organic synthesis. The study of alkyne hydration, reduction, and other transformations highlights the synthetic potential of these unsaturated hydrocarbons.

Aromaticity: The Resonance Dance of Benzene

Aromatic compounds, exemplified by benzene, represent a special class of unsaturated hydrocarbons with exceptional stability and unique reactivity. We unravel the concept of aromaticity, understanding how the cyclic delocalization of π electrons imparts stability to aromatic compounds. The study of electrophilic aromatic substitution reveals the radiochemistry and mechanism of reactions involving aromatic rings.

Heterocycles: Aromaticity Beyond Carbon Rings

Heterocycles, containing atoms other than carbon in their aromatic rings, expand the realm of aromatic chemistry. We explore the aromaticity of heterocyclic compounds, recognizing the importance of nitrogen, oxygen, and other heteroatoms in influencing the stability and reactivity of these compounds. Examples of heterocycles, such as pyridine and furan, showcase the diverse applications of aromaticity in organic synthesis.

Synthetic Strategies: From Functional Group Transformations to Total Synthesis

Organic synthesis involves the construction of complex molecules from simpler starting materials through a series of chemical reactions. We delve into synthetic strategies, understanding how functional group transformations and strategic disconnections guide the design of synthetic routes. The concept of retrosynthetic analysis becomes a powerful tool in planning the synthesis of target molecules.

Conclusion: Organic Chemistry as the Molecular Composer of Nature and Synthesis

In the exploration of organic chemistry fundamentals, we uncover the molecular symphony orchestrated by carbon, a symphony that permeates the diversity of life and the vast landscape of synthetic molecules. Armed with the principles of organic chemistry, degree students are equipped to decipher the language of carbon-containing compounds, predicting their structures, reactivity, and potential transformations.

As our expedition through the "Foundations of Modern Chemistry" continues, the insights gained from the study of organic chemistry will resonate in subsequent chapters. From the intricacies of reaction mechanisms to the dynamic world of bioorganic chemistry, organic chemistry stands as the molecular composer upon which the edifice of chemical understanding is erected.

14.INORGANIC CHEMISTRY

Transition Metals and Coordination Complexes

I n the vast landscape of chemistry, inorganic chemistry stands as a pillar that explores the properties and behaviour of inorganic compounds, distinct from the carbon-centric focus of organic chemistry. Within this domain, the study of transition metals and coordination complexes emerges as a captivating and essential area, shedding light on the unique electronic structures and diverse reactivities of these compounds. As we delve into the "Foundations of Modern Chemistry: A Comprehensive Guide for Degree Students," our focus turns to the intricate world of transition metals and their coordination chemistry.

Introduction to Transition Metals: The Elements of Change

The transition metals, comprising elements in the d-block of the periodic table, exhibit a distinctive array of properties that set them apart from other elements. We explore the electronic configurations of transition metals, understanding the filling of d orbitals and the phenomenon of electron shielding. The variability in oxidation states and the formation of coloured compounds mark the transition metals as elements of change, laying the foundation for their rich chemistry.

Electronic Configurations of Transition Metals: The Dazzling Dance of Electrons

The filling of d orbitals in transition metals introduces a dynamic interplay of electrons, leading to a multitude of possible oxidation states. We unravel the principles behind the electronic configurations of transition metals, recognizing the role of Hund's rule and the Aufbau principle. The concept of effective nuclear charge emerges as a guiding factor in understanding the stability of different oxidation states.

Variable Oxidation States: The Chameleon-like Nature of Transition Metals

One of the defining features of transition metals is their ability to exist in multiple oxidation states. We explore the concept of oxidation states, understanding how the loss or gain of electrons in d orbitals leads to the formation of cations with different charges. The chameleon-like nature of transition metals, transitioning between oxidation states, forms the basis for their involvement in a diverse array of chemical reactions.

Coordination Chemistry: The Art of Molecular Ties

Coordination complexes, at the heart of inorganic chemistry, involve the coordination of metal ions with surrounding ligands. We delve into the fundamental principles of coordination chemistry, understanding the bonding between metal ions and ligands, the geometry of coordination complexes, and the electronic structure that governs their properties.

Ligands: The Dance Partners of Transition Metals

Ligands, molecules or ions that donate electron pairs to a metal centre, play a pivotal role in the formation of coordination complexes. We explore the diverse types of ligands, from simple monodentate ligands to more complex polydentate ligands, and understand how their properties influence the stability and reactivity of coordination complexes. The concept of chelation, where a ligand forms multiple bonds with a metal centre, adds a layer of complexity to coordination chemistry.

Coordination Number and Geometry: The Spatial Arrangement of Bonds

The coordination number, representing the number of ligands surrounding a metal centre, determines the geometry of a coordination complex. We unravel the relationship between coordination number and geometry, exploring common geometries such as octahedral, tetrahedral, and square planar. The understanding of coordination geometry becomes crucial in predicting the properties and reactivity of coordination complexes.

Crystal Field Theory: A Molecular Ballet in Transition

Crystal Field Theory (CFT) provides a framework for understanding the electronic structure of transition metal complexes by considering the interactions between metal d orbitals and ligands. We delve into the principles of CFT, exploring how ligands influence the energy levels of metal d orbitals and lead to the splitting of these orbitals into sets of higher and lower energy. The concept of crystal field splitting diagrams becomes a tool for predicting the colors and magnetic properties of coordination complexes.

Octahedral and Tetrahedral Complexes: Symmetry in Motion

The application of CFT to octahedral and tetrahedral complexes reveals the symmetry in motion of metal d orbitals. We explore how the interaction with ligands leads to the splitting of d orbitals into sets of higher and lower energy levels. The interpretation of crystal field splitting diagrams for octahedral and tetrahedral complexes provides insights into the electronic structure and stability of these coordination geometries.

Square Planar and Linear Complexes: Beyond the Ordinary

Beyond octahedral and tetrahedral complexes, transition metals can form square planar and linear complexes. We unravel the electronic structure of square planar and linear coordination geometries, understanding how the coordination number and ligand field strength influence the arrangement of metal d orbitals. The exploration of unusual coordination geometries showcases the versatility of transition metals in forming diverse coordination complexes.

Colors and Magnetism of Transition Metal Complexes: The Visual and Magnetic Symphony

One of the striking features of transition metal complexes is their vivid colors and magnetic properties. We explore the origins of colour in coordination complexes, understanding how the interaction between light and transition metal electrons leads to the absorption of certain wavelengths and the display of complementary colors. The study of magnetic behaviour, influenced by the presence of unpaired electrons, adds another dimension to the characterization of transition metal complexes.

Origin of Colors: Electronic Transitions and Absorption Spectra

The colour of transition metal complexes arises from electronic transitions involving d orbitals. We delve into the principles behind these electronic transitions, understanding how the absorption of light leads to the promotion of electrons from lower to higher energy d orbitals. The interpretation of absorption spectra becomes a valuable tool in identifying the electronic transitions responsible for the observed colors of coordination complexes.

Magnetic Properties: The Dance of Unpaired Electrons

The presence of unpaired electrons in transition metal complexes imparts magnetic behaviour. We explore the principles of magnetism in coordination complexes, understanding how the alignment of magnetic moments and the interaction between magnetic centres influence the overall magnetic properties. The interpretation of magnetic behaviour provides insights into the electronic structure and bonding in transition metal complexes.

Isomerism in Coordination Complexes: A Molecular Jigsaw Puzzle

Isomerism in coordination complexes adds an additional layer of complexity to the study of transition metal chemistry. We explore different types of isomerism, including geometric isomerism, structural isomerism, and optical isomerism, understanding how the arrangement of ligands around a metal centre influences the properties of coordination complexes. The recognition of isomers becomes essential in characterizing and predicting the behaviour of transition metal complexes.

Geometric Isomerism: A Spatial Tango of Ligands

Geometric isomerism, arising from different spatial arrangements of ligands, introduces a tango of isomers in coordination complexes. We unravel the concept of cis-trans isomerism, understanding how the placement of ligands in relation to each other influences the properties of coordination complexes. The study of geometric isomerism becomes a dynamic exploration of the spatial dance of ligands around a central metal ion.

Structural Isomerism: Rearranging Ligands in the Molecular Landscape

Structural isomerism encompasses different arrangements of ligands in coordination complexes. We explore the distinctions between linkage isomerism, coordination isomerism, and ionization isomerism, understanding how changes in the connectivity and composition of ligands result in structurally distinct isomers. The identification of structural isomers becomes a molecular jigsaw puzzle in the characterization of coordination complexes.

Reactivity of Transition Metal Complexes: Beyond Stability to Catalysis

The reactivity of transition metal complexes extends beyond their stability and electronic structure to encompass a wide range of chemical transformations. We explore the principles of ligand substitution, redox reactions, and catalysis in transition metal complexes, recognizing their pivotal role in industrial processes and biological systems.

Ligand Substitution: The Dance of Ligands in Transition

Ligand substitution reactions involve the exchange of one or more ligands in a coordination complex. We unravel the mechanisms of ligand substitution, understanding how factors such as ligand field strength, steric hindrance, and electronic configuration influence the kinetics and thermodynamics of these reactions. The study of ligand substitution becomes a dynamic exploration of the dance of ligands around a central metal ion.

Redox Reactions: Electron Transfer Ballet in Transition Metal Complexes

Redox reactions involving transition metal complexes showcase the ability of these compounds to undergo electron transfer. We explore the principles of redox reactions in coordination complexes, understanding how changes in oxidation states and the transfer of electrons between metal ions and ligands drive chemical transformations. The study of redox reactions becomes a ballet of electron transfer, influencing the reactivity and stability of transition metal complexes.

Catalysis: Transition Metals as Molecular Choreographers

Transition metals play a crucial role in catalysis, serving as molecular choreographers that accelerate chemical reactions. We delve into the principles of catalysis by transition metal complexes, understanding how they lower activation energies, stabilize reaction intermediates, and enable the selective formation of desired products. The study of catalysis becomes a bridge between fundamental principles and practical applications in the synthesis of pharmaceuticals, polymers, and other industrially important compounds.

Bioinorganic Chemistry: Transition Metals in Biological Systems

The influence of transition metals extends into the realm of biology, where they play essential roles in enzymatic reactions, oxygen transport, and electron transfer processes. We explore the principles of bioinorganic chemistry, understanding how transition metals such as iron, copper, and zinc function as cofactors in biological macromolecules. The study of metalloenzymes and metalloproteins becomes a window into the intersection of inorganic chemistry and the intricacies of living organisms.

Metalloenzymes: Transition Metals in Catalytic Roles

Metalloenzymes, enzymes that contain metal cofactors, showcase the catalytic prowess of transition metals in biological systems. We unravel the mechanisms of metalloenzymes, understanding how metal ions facilitate the activation of substrates and the formation of reaction intermediates. The study of metalloenzymes becomes a glimpse into the finely tuned choreography of chemical transformations in living organisms.

Metalloproteins: Transition Metals as Structural Stalwarts

Transition metals also serve as structural components in metalloproteins, influencing their stability and function. We explore the role of metal ions in stabilizing protein structures, mediating protein-protein interactions, and participating in electron transfer processes. The study of metalloproteins becomes an exploration of the structural and functional diversity of transition metals in biological systems.

Conclusion: Transition Metals as Molecular Architects and Biological Conductors

In the exploration of transition metals and coordination complexes, we uncover the fascinating world of molecular architecture and reactivity that defines the chemistry of these elements. From the dynamic electronic configurations of transition metals to the spatial dance of ligands in coordination complexes, the principles unveiled in this journey resonate across the realms of inorganic chemistry, catalysis, and bioinorganic chemistry.

As our expedition through the "Foundations of Modern Chemistry" continues, the insights gained from the study of transition metals will intertwine with other branches of chemistry. From the microscopic intricacies of molecular reactions to the macroscopic applications in materials science and medicine, transition metals stand as molecular architects and biological conductors upon which the edifice of chemical understanding is erected.

15.ENVIRONMENTAL CHEMISTRY AND SUSTAINABLE PRACTICES

I n the dynamic interplay between human activities and the environment, environmental chemistry emerges as a vital discipline that explores the impact of chemical processes on the Earth's ecosystems. As we navigate through the "Foundations of Modern Chemistry: A Comprehensive Guide for Degree Students," our focus turns to the essential principles of environmental chemistry and the imperative of sustainable practices. In this exploration, we delve into the intricate web of chemical interactions shaping our environment and the role of sustainable practices in preserving the delicate balance of our planet.

Introduction to Environmental Chemistry: The Chemical Tapestry of Earth

Environmental chemistry is the branch of chemistry dedicated to understanding the chemical processes occurring in the environment and their implications for human health and ecosystems. It encompasses a broad spectrum of topics, from the study of pollutants and their sources to the analysis of natural processes that maintain the equilibrium of ecosystems.

Sources and Types of Environmental Pollutants: Unravelling the Chemical Threads

Environmental pollutants, originating from natural and anthropogenic sources, pose a significant challenge to the health of the planet. We explore the various types of pollutants, including air pollutants, water contaminants, soil pollutants, and persistent organic pollutants. Understanding the sources and behaviours of these pollutants becomes a fundamental step in devising strategies for their mitigation and remediation.

Chemical Cycling in the Environment: The Dance of Elements

The environment is a dynamic arena where elements engage in intricate cycles that sustain life. We unravel the chemical cycling of elements, such as the nitrogen and phosphorus cycles, which play critical roles in the functioning of ecosystems. The study of biogeochemical cycles provides insights into how chemical elements move through the atmosphere, hydrosphere, and lithosphere, influencing the health of living organisms and the stability of ecosystems.

Air Quality and Atmospheric Chemistry: The Breath of Life in Jeopardy

The quality of the air we breathe is intricately linked to atmospheric chemistry, where natural and anthropogenic processes shape the composition of the atmosphere. We delve into the sources and effects of air pollutants, including greenhouse gases, ozone-depleting substances, and particulate matter. Understanding atmospheric reactions and the factors influencing air quality becomes essential in addressing the challenges of urban air pollution and global climate change.

Greenhouse Gases and Global Warming: The Heat-Trapping Blanket

The increase in greenhouse gas concentrations, primarily carbon dioxide (CO_2) and methane (CH_4), contributes to global warming and climate change. We explore the mechanisms behind the greenhouse effect, understanding how certain gases trap heat in the Earth's atmosphere. The consequences of climate change, including rising temperatures, sea-level rise, and extreme weather events, underscore the urgency of mitigating greenhouse gas emissions.

Stratospheric Ozone Depletion: The Threatened Shield

The ozone layer in the stratosphere plays a crucial role in protecting life on Earth by absorbing harmful ultraviolet (UV) radiation. We unravel the chemistry behind ozone depletion, particularly the role of human-made substances like chlorofluorocarbons (CFCs) in depleting stratospheric ozone. The successful international efforts to address ozone depletion through the Montreal Protocol serve as a beacon of hope for global environmental cooperation.

Water Chemistry and Quality: Liquid Gold in Peril

Water, a precious resource, is intricately linked to environmental chemistry through processes such as hydrolysis, acid-base reactions, and the cycling of nutrients. We explore the chemistry of water pollutants, including heavy metals, pesticides, and nutrients, and their effects on aquatic ecosystems. The study of water quality becomes imperative for safeguarding human health, sustaining biodiversity, and ensuring the availability of clean water for future generations.

Nutrient Pollution: The Unseen Culprit

Excessive nutrient inputs, particularly nitrogen and phosphorus from agricultural runoff and wastewater discharges, contribute to nutrient pollution in water bodies. We unravel the impacts of nutrient pollution, including harmful algal blooms, oxygen depletion, and the creation of "dead zones" in aquatic ecosystems. Sustainable agricultural practices and wastewater treatment strategies become crucial in addressing the root causes of nutrient pollution.

Heavy Metals in Water: Tracing the Toxic Trails

Heavy metals, such as mercury, lead, and cadmium, pose significant threats to water quality and aquatic life. We explore the sources, distribution, and toxicity of heavy metals in water bodies, understanding how they accumulate in organisms and pose risks to human health through the consumption of contaminated seafood. The implementation of pollution prevention measures and the development of innovative remediation technologies become key components in mitigating the impacts of heavy metal pollution.

Soil Chemistry and Contamination: The Earth Beneath Our Feet

The health of soil ecosystems is intimately tied to soil chemistry, where natural processes and human activities influence the availability of nutrients, the pH of the soil, and the fate of contaminants. We delve into the mechanisms of soil contamination, including the leaching of pesticides, the accumulation of heavy metals, and the persistence of organic pollutants. Sustainable soil management practices, such as organic farming and phytoremediation, offer pathways to restore soil health and fertility.

Pesticides and Soil Health: Balancing Act in Agriculture

Pesticides, essential for crop protection, can have unintended consequences on soil health and ecosystems. We explore the chemistry of pesticides, understanding their modes of action, persistence in the environment, and potential impacts on non-target organisms. Integrated pest management (IPM) practices and the development of environmentally friendly pesticides become crucial in achieving a balance between agricultural productivity and environmental sustainability.

Phytoremediation: Plants as Environmental Clean-up Artists

Phytoremediation harnesses the natural abilities of plants to extract, accumulate, and detoxify pollutants from the soil. We unravel the mechanisms behind phytoremediation, understanding how certain plants, known as hyperaccumulators, can remediate soils contaminated with heavy metals, organic pollutants, and even radioactive substances. The application of phytoremediation offers a sustainable and cost-effective approach to soil remediation.

Waste Management and Green Chemistry: Closing the Loop Responsibly

The management of waste, from its generation to disposal, is a critical aspect of environmental chemistry. We explore the principles of green chemistry, which seeks to design products and processes that minimize environmental impact. The concepts of reduce, reuse, and recycle become guiding principles in waste management, aiming to minimize the environmental footprint of human activities.

Solid Waste Management: Rethinking the Disposables

The disposal of solid waste, including plastics, electronic waste, and household refuse, poses significant challenges to environmental sustainability. We delve into the environmental impacts of different types of solid waste, understanding the principles of landfill management, recycling, and waste-to-energy technologies. Sustainable practices, such as the reduction of single-use plastics and the promotion of circular economies, become essential in addressing the global solid waste crisis.

Green Chemistry: Designing for Sustainability

Green chemistry emphasizes the design of chemical products and processes that reduce or eliminate the use and generation of hazardous substances. We explore the principles of green chemistry, including the use of renewable feedstocks, the reduction of waste, and the development of safer chemical alternatives. Sustainable practices in chemical manufacturing and the adoption of green chemistry principles contribute to the transition towards a more sustainable and environmentally friendly chemical industry.

Sustainable Energy: Powering the Future Responsibly

The quest for sustainable energy sources is at the forefront of addressing environmental challenges, particularly the impact of fossil fuel combustion on air quality and climate change. We explore the chemistry of renewable energy sources, including solar, wind, and bioenergy, understanding the principles behind their generation and the potential for reducing reliance on non-renewable resources.

Solar Energy: Harnessing the Power of the Sun

Solar energy, derived from the sun's radiation, presents a clean and abundant source of power. We unravel the chemistry behind solar photovoltaic cells, understanding how sunlight is converted into electricity. Advances in solar cell technology, including the development of perovskite solar cells, hold promise for increasing the efficiency and affordability of solar energy.

Wind Energy: Tapping into Nature's Kinetic Force

Wind energy harnesses the kinetic energy of moving air to generate electricity. We explore the chemistry behind wind turbines, understanding the role of materials such as rare earth metals in the production of efficient wind generators. The expansion of wind energy infrastructure and the integration of wind power into the grid contribute to a more sustainable and resilient energy system.

Bioenergy: Turning Biomass into Fuel

Bioenergy involves the conversion of biomass, such as plant residues and organic waste, into energy. We delve into the chemistry of bioenergy processes, including biomass combustion, bioethanol production, and biodiesel synthesis. Sustainable practices in bioenergy emphasize the responsible management of biomass resources, the reduction of greenhouse gas emissions, and the promotion of energy independence.

Conclusion: A Call to Action for Tomorrow's Chemists

As we navigate the realms of environmental chemistry and sustainable practices, the interconnectedness of chemical processes with the health of the planet becomes evident. From the air we breathe to the water we drink and the soil beneath our feet, chemistry plays a pivotal role in shaping the environmental landscape. The principles of sustainability, rooted in responsible chemical practices and a holistic understanding of environmental systems, pave the way for a harmonious coexistence between human activities and the Earth.

The "Foundations of Modern Chemistry" serve not only as a guide for degree students but also as a call to action for tomorrow's chemists. Armed with the knowledge gained from this comprehensive exploration, students are empowered to become stewards of the environment, advocates for sustainable practices, and catalysts for positive change. The future of chemistry lies not only in the laboratories but also in the classrooms, boardrooms, and policy arenas where decisions are made that impact the delicate balance of our planet. Through a collective commitment to environmental responsibility and sustainable chemistry, the foundations we lay today will shape a resilient and thriving world for generations to come.

Milton Keynes UK
Ingram Content Group UK Ltd.
UKHW030636201123
432908UK00017B/2186

9 798223 080381